Rock in Sequence

An Anthology of Pop for Sequencing

William Lloyd *and* **Paul Terry**

• Musonix Publishing •

In memory of Martin Vafadari (1964–1992)

Other music technology titles from Musonix:

Music in Sequence – A complete guide to MIDI sequencing
Classics in Sequence – A source book for MIDI sequencing
The Studio Musician's Jargonbuster – A glossary of music technology and recording
Composing in Sequence *(in preparation)*

First published in 1996   ISBN Number   0 9517214 5 3

Published by Musonix Publishing, 2 Avenue Gardens, London SW14 8BP.

Exclusive distributors: Music Sales Limited   Music Sales Corporation   Music Sales Pty.
                            8/9 Frith Street   257 Park Avenue South   120 Rothschild Avenue
                            London   W1V 5TZ   New York   NY 10010   USA   Rosebery, NSW 2018   Australia

                            Order Number: MX 30079

Cover design by Bob Linney

At The Hop. Words & Music by A. Singer, J. Medora & D. White. © Copyright 1957 Arc Music Corporation, USA. Tristan Music Limited, 22 Denmark Street, London WC2. *
Shboom (Life Could Be A Dream). Words & Music by Carl Feaster, Claude Feaster, James Keyes, James Edwards & Floyd McRae. © Copyright 1954 Hill & Range Songs Incorporated / Brenner Music Incorporated, USA. Carlin Music Corporation, Iron Bridge House, 3 Bridge Approach, London NW1. *
Bony Moronie. Words & Music by Larry Williams. © 1957 & 1966 Venice Music Incorporated, USA. Venice Music Limited, 127 Charing Cross Road, London WC2. *
Puppy Love. Words & Music by Paul Anka. © 1959 & 1972 Spanka Music Corporation, USA. MAM (Music Publishing) Limited / Chrysalis Music Limited, The Old Phoenix Brewery, Bramley Road, London W10. *
Please Please Me. Words & Music by John Lennon & Paul McCartney. © Copyright 1962 Dick James Music Limited, 47 British Grove, London W4. *
A Whiter Shade Of Pale. Words & Music by Keith Reid & Gary Brooker. © Copyright 1967 by Onward Music Limited, 1A Farm Place, London W8. *
He Ain't Heavy … He's My Brother. Words by Bob Russell, Music by Bobby Scott. © Copyright 1969 by Harrison Music Corporation, USA & Jenny Music. Chelsea Music Publishing Company Limited, 70 Gloucester Place, London W1H 4AJ / Jenny Music. *
Black Magic Woman. Words & Music by Peter A. Green. © Copyright 1968 & 1970 by Bourne-King Publishing Company Ltd., London W1R 9PD. Used by permission of Bourne Music Limited, 2/5 Old Bond Street, London W1X 3TB. All Rights Reserved. International Copyright Secured.
Stairway To Heaven. Words & Music by Jimmy Page & Robert Plant. © Copyright 1972 Superhype Music Inc. Warner Chappell Music Ltd., London W1Y 3FA. Reproduced by permission of International Music Publications Limited.
I Do It For Your Love. Words & Music by Paul Simon. © Copyright 1975 Paul Simon. *
Money, Money, Money. Words & Music by Benny Andersson & Björn Ulvaeus. © Copyright 1976 by Union Songs AB, Stockholm, Sweden for the world. Bocu Music Limited, 1 Wyndham Yard, Wyndham Place, London W1 for Great Britain and Eire. *
Rivers of Babylon. Words & Music by Farian, Reyam, Dowe and McNaughton. © Copyright Far Musikverlag and Beverleys Records for the world. © Copyright 1978 Far Musikverlag Gmbh / Hansa Productions Limited. Blue Mountain Music Limited for the UK and Eire. *
Hello. Words & Music by Lionel Ritchie. © Copyright 1983, 1984 Brockman Music, USA. Rondor Music (London) Limited, 10a Parsons Green, London SW6. *
Money For Nothing. Words & Music by Mark Knopfler & Sting. © Copyright 1985 Chariscourt Limited / Rondor Music (London) Limited / Magnetic Publishing Limited, London. *
It's Alright (Baby's Coming Back). Words & Music by A. Lennox & D. A. Stewart. © 1985 D'N'A Limited / BMG Music Publishing Limited. All rights administered by BMG Music Publishing Limited, Bedford House, 69–79 Fulham High Street, London SW6 3JW. This arrangement © Copyright 1995 BMG Music Publishing Limited. *
Straight To My Heart. Words & Music by Sting. © Copyright 1987 G. M. Sumner. Magnetic Music Publishing Limited, London W1. *
Best Days. Words & Music by Damon Albarn, Graham Coxon, Alex James & David Rowntree. © Copyright 1995 MCA Music Limited, 77 Fulham Palace Road, London W6. *

* Used by permission of Music Sales Limited. All Rights Reserved. International Copyright Secured.

Thanks to Kev Smith for his helpful suggestions

Printed and bound in Great Britain by
Caligraving Limited Thetford Norfolk

Contents

Introduction

We have used the term 'rock' to embrace a huge variety of popular music from the 1950s to the present day. Any anthology involves a process of selection, and we have regretfully had to jettison many favourite songs that could have appeared had space permitted. Our choice has been dictated by three aims: to include songs, some familiar and others less so, whose qualities have stood the test of time; music that will give some idea of the rich variety of styles in popular music over the last forty years, and (above all) tracks that can be recreated convincingly by you on the sequencer.

Each song is presented in a format which will allow you to make full use of the enormous musical resources at your disposal. This includes explanatory text, with many useful tips and graphic illustrations, to support the printed scores. These scores are detailed transcriptions which we hope will assist you in reproducing many of the nuances of the original recordings which are listed in the Discography on page 110. We have included lyrics for those who want to sing along, but also give suggestions for making purely instrumental versions. In just a few cases we have transposed songs or slightly re-arranged backing tracks where the originals would be awkward to input from the keyboard.

Rock music is endlessly adept at re-cycling itself and each new performance of a song has something fresh to add to the original. Remember that a printed score is more of a snapshot than a definitive version and is often little more than an afterthought for many rock musicians. We hope that creating your own unique performances of these songs will not only be hugely enjoyable, but will also lead you, as it has led us, to a greater understanding of the music itself and how it is put together.

If you are new to sequencing, we recommend first working through our companion volume, *Music in Sequence*, which deals with some of the basic note-reading and sequencing skills needed in a wide variety of musical styles. As in that book, our aim here is not to present yet another technical manual, but to explain how to interpret music using the technology creatively. We hope you enjoy it.

William Lloyd and Paul Terry

The Sequencing Studio

What you will need

THE BASIC SYSTEM

Sequencers come as software programs for computers and as hardware units that are either free-standing or built into a type of synthesizer known as a **workstation**. Hardware sequencers are robust and easily transportable, making them suitable for live playback work, but recording and editing can be difficult as they generally have tiny display panels and limited editing facilities. A **computer-based** system is a more expensive option, but it provides a full-screen display, a larger memory for sequences and easier operation with the computer's mouse and keyboard. Software can be upgraded as needed, and the computer can also be used for many other musical and non-musical tasks.

The sound generating part of the system is provided by a **synthesizer**. This usually includes a piano-type keyboard although the circuitry may also be available as a computer expansion card, such as the "Sound Blaster". If you take the latter option, a MIDI keyboard will almost certainly still be needed to make input easier.

Modern synthesizers usually offer at least 128 different sounds (**voices**) and most are **multi-timbral** – meaning that they can play a number of these simultaneously with the help of a sequencer. Synth specifications will state the maximum number of multi-timbral parts available – often 16 or more. Don't confuse this with the figure quoted for the synth's *polyphony*, usually 32 or 64, which simply refers to the maximum number of *notes* that can sound together. Many new synthesizers are "GM" compatible, a standardized specification that makes them ideal for sequencing – see the General MIDI Fact Sheet on page 31.

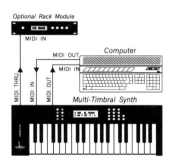

Unless your sequencer is built into the synth, you will need to connect the two with **MIDI leads**. The MIDI OUT from the synth sends electronic data about your playing to the sequencer for recording, while the sequencer's MIDI OUT relays the recorded signals back to the synth for performance (see left). Sound Card users will need just a simple connection from the input keyboard's MIDI OUT to the computer. If you do not wish to work with **headphones**, you will also need a **powered monitor** in order to hear the music. In this context, monitor is another word for a robust loudspeaker: "powered" refers to the fact that it contains its own amplifier. Two of them will be needed for stereo sound. Using a hi-fi amplifier and speakers is not a good idea, as they can easily be damaged by the wide output range of a synth.

EXPANSION

Many users soon feel the need to extend their sound-generating facilities. This can be done simply by adding a **rack module** or **expander** – a sound generator without a keyboard that is controlled from your main synth. For sequencing it can be connected to the system as shown in the diagram – the MIDI THRU socket merely duplicates the data being sent from the sequencer. A **drum machine** can be connected in the same way, although most modern synths include their own wide range of percussion sounds. An increasingly important expander is a **sampler**. Samples are digital recordings of individual live sounds which can be triggered from the keyboard or sequencer: they are generally more realistic than even the best synthesized versions.

EFFECTS

Reverberation and other electronic effects will be essential for most of the sequences in this book, since rock music and technology have developed virtually hand in hand. A **multi-effects** unit is already built into most synth workstations and can be used on individual voices or on the synth's output as a whole. Freestanding units are also available which will be useful for sampled sounds. For more detail on different effects and their uses, see the Fact Sheet on page 53.

RECORDING TO TAPE

You will probably want to record your work. If you use just a single synth you can connect its line outputs directly to an ordinary **stereo cassette recorder**. However, more complex set-ups will really need a basic mixing desk. A four or eight-track **portastudio** can be used for this, although the multi-track recording that these offer will only be needed if you want to add live musicians – and you will still have to produce a two-track tape at the end of the day. The mixing and balancing of the synth tracks is, in any case, best done from the sequencer.

How MIDI works

MIDI MESSAGES

MIDI allows basic performance instructions, such as the pitch and loudness of notes, to be transmitted between pieces of compatible equipment *via* a MIDI lead at a rate of up to 31,250 signals per second. These binary pulses are grouped to form meaningful messages, such as "Note On" – the instruction to start playing a note.

The MIDI Note On message actually consists of three parts: a "status byte" which tells the synth that the command is to turn a note on, followed by two data bytes – detailing the pitch of the note (**note number**) and its loudness (**velocity**).

Clearly, the system also needs to know which synth, or which voice within a multi-timbral synth, is to play this note. For this purpose, the status byte also includes a **channel number** between 1 and 16. Only instruments in the system set to receive on that channel will respond. A multi-timbral synth can listen to a number of channels from the sequencer simultaneously and can play each on a different voice.

The limitation of MIDI to 16 channels can be a problem if you have the synth capacity to play more than 16 voices at once. A MIDI split box will not help – it gives extra sockets but not extra channels. However, special MIDI interfaces are available which provide 64 channels or more, separated into groups of 16, with each set going through a separate MIDI port and cable to the relevant synth.

MIDI is a serial system: it can deal with only one message at a time. In a chord the notes are actually played one after the other in very quick succession, although the ear is deceived by the speed of MIDI into hearing perfectly synchronized notes:

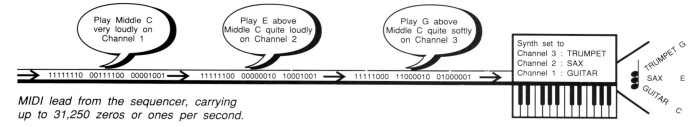

MIDI lead from the sequencer, carrying up to 31,250 zeros or ones per second.

Much more goes on than we can show in the simple diagram above. Every Note On must be followed by a Note Off message, the time between the two dictating the actual note length. MIDI also deals with other types of messages – for changing voices or operating controllers such as modulation wheels and foot pedals. It is even possible to transmit the entire structure of a specially edited synth voice by means of a SysEx (Systems Exclusive) message.

Some actions, such as using aftertouch (pushing hard into a key after the start of a note) can generate huge quantities of MIDI data. In complex pieces it is possible to overload the system, causing "MIDI choke" which can result in data being delayed or lost. More common, though, are problems caused by overloading the synth rather than MIDI – asking for 17 simultaneous notes on a synth with 16-note polyphony, for example, will cut off the first note of the chord when the 17th note arrives.

Almost all the data needed to create the most detailed performance can be carried by MIDI. The manipulation of this digital information, whether the subtle adjustment of note lengths required to articulate rhythm, the sudden loudness of an accent or the careful grading of pitch bend, is where you and the sequencer come in.

Setting up the system

Setting-up a synth for sequencing takes a little time, but should be a once-only procedure, as the settings can be saved in the synth's memory for future use.

In order to receive data on several MIDI channels at the same time, the synth must be in Multi-Timbral (sometimes called Combi) mode and a patch or combination must be selected that can receive on several MIDI channels at once. Although some synths offer many such configurations, only one is needed for all your sequencing, and this should be as uncluttered as possible. If your synth does not offer a suitable preset, create your own as follows:

1. Find an existing combination that you don't mind altering.

2. Check that a different MIDI channel is assigned to each of the instruments within the patch. It is probably simplest to use consecutive channel numbers: perhaps 1-10 on your main synth, leaving 11-16 for a second synth or expander if you have one.

Setting Instrument 3 to Channel 4, voiced for Tenor Sax 67, in a multi-timbral combination. The sound is Panned left and has output Level set to maximum 127.

3. Select a clear voice for each channel. It is unimportant precisely which sounds you choose, as each sequence can reset this part of the combination. You may care to set a group of standard sounds ready for use with the music in this book, such as Sax, Trumpet, Strings, Electric Guitar, Bass Guitar, Piano and Drum Kit. It has become something of a tradition to assign drums to channel 10, and this convention is maintained in GM compatible equipment.

4. Make sure that each instrument is set to be available at maximum output level, with no unwanted transposition in operation, and able to operate over the entire pitch range (*ie* not limited by a pitch "window").

5. Each voice should have MIDI program change, controller and aftertouch enabled ("filters off") as these are features required by many of the sequences in this book.

6. Functions such as detuning and effects (*eg* reverb) can be set as desired. Some panning of channels to left and right will give a rough impression of stereo space – more specific placing can be achieved from the sequencer.

7. Re-name the combination, if necessary, and save it in your synth's internal memory.

Your synth manual should show you how to do all this and how to save the settings. Then you only need to turn the equipment on at the start of a session and select your sequencing patch on the synth in order to start.

GLOBAL CHANNEL

Some synths use one channel (known sometimes as the global or common channel) for certain operations which affect the instrument as a whole. This is usually MIDI channel 1, although it can be reassigned. A voice number set on the sequencer for the global channel *may* throw the synth into entirely the wrong combination. There is no quick solution to this problem and (if it affects your system) it is probably easiest to change the global channel to some number that you will not use in your sequences.

While the synth has been set to listen to a number of channels simultaneously, it normally only transmits on one channel at a time (usually the global channel). So, even though you may hear the sax sound that you assigned to, say, channel 2, during playback, the synth may annoyingly produce a quite different voice as you record:

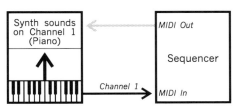

A piano sound is heard when recording

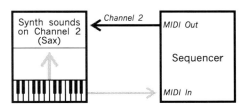

A sax sound is heard on playback

This is not ideal: it is much better to record using the right voice, as you can then match your playing style to the characteristics of the sound you want.

**LOCAL OFF &
MIDI THRU**

To get round this problem, most synths allow you to sever the connection between the keyboard and sound generator by setting a switch in the synth called **Local** to off. The signal then goes only to your sequencer, in which another switch called **MIDI Thru** immediately echoes the data back to the synth along the return MIDI lead, but now on channel 2 so that the intended sax voice is heard while you play:

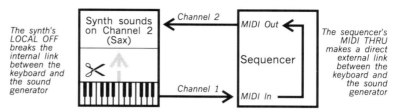

A sax sound is now heard on both recording and playback

If you use this MIDI Thru facility it is important to switch Local off in the synth, otherwise every note will be played twice – once directly through the local connection, and again upon being echoed back from the sequencer. Even if you don't notice the double notes, they will quickly eat up your synth's polyphony and notes will thus start to disappear from thick textures.

The MIDI Thru facility is also needed if your system consists of a master keyboard (which has no sound generator of its own), computer and separate rack module. You don't need to worry about Local off, of course, because the keyboard and sound generator are not connected except by MIDI.

SYSTEMS EXCLUSIVE   You may find you want to program your synth to suit a particular sequence – for example, a specific pitch bend range, some extra reverb on drums, or a specially edited trumpet sound. You will probably not wish to make these changes permanent for all sequences by saving them in the synth's memory. The Data Dump facility on many synths provides a way of transmitting these settings via MIDI, so they can be saved with the individual sequence. The sequencer recognises this information as a Systems Exclusive (SysEx) message – data that is exclusive to the type of synth you are using.

Before you make a data dump, check that neither the synth nor the sequencer are filtering out SysEx, and remember that a lot of data is likely to be involved. Transmission can take several seconds and will prevent any other MIDI data being sent at the same time. For this reason it is best to send the dump back before the start of the song. Synth manuals provide information which will enable keen programmers to write their own, specifically targeted, SysEx messages directly into a sequence – useful for re-setting pitch bend range in the middle of a song, for example.

Multimedia and Sound Cards

A **sound card** is a keyboardless synthesizer built onto a printed circuit board that fits into one of the expansion slots of a personal computer. The first models, appearing in the late '80s, were designed primarily to add sound to computer games programs, but more recent versions typically include an optional MIDI interface, stereo output and the capability to record and replay digital samples.

A sound card is supplied with **multimedia** computers, along with small monitor speakers and (usually) a simple sequencing program. You are still likely to need a MIDI keyboard (a silent "keyboard controller" will do), unless you are prepared to input all your sequences by mouse clicking. Many people find a multimedia setup a convenient and compact system for sequencing – and the capability to access the Internet allows sequencer junkies to exchange files around the globe. However, on the down side, remember that the synth sounds may be disappointing on the cheapest sound cards and that very small monitor speakers can also limit quality.

Using The Sequencer

This guide gives an overview of useful sequencer functions. The names and appearance of some features may be a little different on your own sequencer, but it will probably have most of the facilities listed here. Practical uses for many of these features will be found throughout this book, and its companions, **Music in Sequence** *and* **Classics in Sequence***.*

TRACKS & PARTS

When music is recorded into a sequencer it is stored as a series of **tracks**. These are the horizontal layers of your music and most sequencers allow you to divide them into shorter sections called **parts** (or patterns):

	Bar Numbers	1	5	9	13	17	21	24
Track 1	Lead Guitar			Chorus		Verse		Chorus
Track 2	Bass	Intro		Chorus		Verse		Chorus
Track 3	Drums	Intro		Chorus		Verse		Chorus

In this example, there are three tracks: the identifying labels, like *Lead Guitar,* can be typed in by the user. Similarly, each part can usually be given a name, such as *Intro,* to show its position in the music. Sequencers often allow you to **group** several parts or tracks together, so that they can be moved and worked on as a single unit.

The complete set-up of parts, tracks and instrumental voices that you choose to assign to those tracks is generally known as the **arrangement**.

Each individual instrumental line is normally recorded onto a different track. Software sequencers offer more empty tracks than you will ever use. Don't be afraid to separate the strands of complex music, such as the treble and bass staves of piano music or the separate instruments within a drum kit, and put them onto different tracks.

MIDI CHANNELS & VOICE NUMBERS

Typing names into a track or part may be helpful to you but it is pretty meaningless to the synth that will play your music. In order for each track to use a different sound, it will have to be given a different MIDI channel number. If you want it to play on a voice other than the one already assigned to this channel in the synth, you will also need to set the voice number you require.

For example, if you set Track 2 to Channel 7 on the sequencer, and assign voice 23 to it, the synth will play the music using voice 23 – providing its multi-timbral patch is set to receive on Channel 7. Any voice already allocated on the synth will be over-ridden by the sequencer, unless either has been set to filter out voice changes (also called **program** changes). If your sequencer starts counting voices from 1 while the synth counts them from 0 you will always need to add one when making program changes in the sequence. Synths with more than 128 voices will need a sequencer that implements a **bank select** function to access voice numbers beyond this limit.

TRANSPORT CONTROLS

Most sequencers use icons that look like the controls of a cassette recorder for functions such as play, record, stop *etc*. Certain keys on the computer keyboard can be used to perform the same operations – the manual will give details of these. Keys which take you to the beginning of the sequence, or which start and stop playback are particularly handy, especially for those who dislike using a mouse. It is also possible for some sequencers to assign notes on the synth keyboard for triggering such functions remotely *via* MIDI.

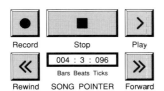

Of course, you also need to know where you are in the music, and for this the sequencer's equivalent of the tape counter is the **song pointer** (bar counter). This shows the bar and beat number, together with the exact position within that beat. This is usually expressed as a number of ticks, with a quarter note typically divided into 192 ticks – although some sequencers can offer even higher resolution. The example on the left shows a song position of bar 4, beat 3½.

00 : 00 : 16 : 12
SMPTE

Hours : Mins : Secs : Frames

5 : 1 : 000	8 : 1 : 000
Left Locator	Right Locator

Many sequencers also have a SMPTE counter (the acronym stands for Society of Motion Picture and Television Engineers). SMPTE is used to synchronize sound with film or video pictures, but is also useful for showing how far into a sequence you are in time (see left). The frame refers to a single still picture on conventional film. Frame rates can be adjusted between 24 and 30 per second, depending on the synchronization system required.

Two other counters often found are the **left and right locators**. These enable you to isolate a specific part of your music (say, bar 5 to the start of bar 8) to be used for a particular operation, such as making a **loop** (cycle) for playback or perhaps for recording in just these specific bars.

Recording

**TEMPO &
TIME SIGNATURES**

One of the advantages that the sequencer has over a standard tape recorder is its ability to play music at any speed (**tempo**) without affecting the pitch. A recording can therefore be made at whatever pace is comfortable and yet still be played back at the correct tempo. It is even possible to record notes one at a time (see *step time* below).

Tempo is measured in beats per minute (**bpm**) and can be set in a range from 16 to 240 bpm or more. Because the sequencer organizes its information in bars and beats, you will also need to set a **time signature** indicating the number of beats per bar. This information is usually entered on the sequencer's main screen, and some will have a special tempo **mastertrack** for setting changes in tempo or time signature during the course of the sequence.

To keep you in time when recording, each beat is sounded by the **metronome**. This can be output either as an electronic beep from the computer or as a MIDI "click" which can sound any note on any channel you select. A **pre-count** (lead-in) of one or two bars will enable you to hear the tempo before recording starts. Many musicians find the beep option distracting and unmusical. You may find it more intuitive to send the MIDI click to a drum kit voice and have each beat played on, say, wood block.

TIP A further alternative, with many rock sequences, is to input the drum part first and use it as rhythmic backing for recording the other tracks. This will help you to get the right feel for playing the rest of the sequence, particularly the bass part whose interaction with the drums is crucial to the success of most rock music.

**RECORDING
OPTIONS**

The start point of a recording is usually set by entering a bar number in the left locator box or by positioning a cursor on the screen. Sometimes you will want to record a section in the middle of a track without affecting existing material on either side of it. This is called **punch-in** recording and will need to have start and end (**punch-out**) positions set in the locator boxes.

Sequencers generally offer two recording modes. **Replace** will, like a tape recorder, erase any existing material on the track. **Overdub**, on the other hand, will add new material without deleting anything already recorded. This is very useful if you want to input complex or chordal music one line at a time.

It is not necessary to record music in **real time** – that is, played in rhythm, however slowly. Notes can be entered in **step time**, where you specify the type of note length required, and then play at leisure without the need to keep to a regular metronome beat. Fast-moving music can be recorded easily and accurately with this method and it is particularly useful when there are many notes of the same length to record. Step time input can be made from the keyboard or by clicking the mouse on screen. However, be aware that the mouse will input all velocities at a uniform preset level, and both methods will place notes mechanically on regular sub-divisions of the beat, giving a lack of freedom that may not be appropriate for the music.

Finally, although we have assumed that most users will record their sequences from a keyboard, other options for input are available which non-keyboard players may prefer. These include MIDI guitar, wind and string controllers, and MIDI drum pads. If you already play a musical instrument, it is likely that somewhere you will find its

Editing

NOTE EDITING

Most sequencers offer several ways of viewing and editing notes and other MIDI information in a part or track:

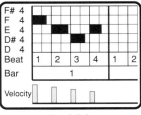

Grid Edit

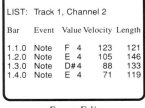

Event Edit

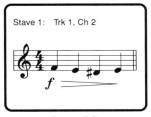

Score Edit

The graphic display on the left is a **grid edit** (also called a "piano roll" after the punched paper roll that triggered notes in old player pianos). It shows the pitch, position and length of each note, any of which can be altered using the computer's mouse. Additional information, such as individual **velocity** (loudness) levels, can be called up and adjusted and notes may be copied, moved or erased.

The **event edit** (or list edit) system deals largely in numbers and is useful for really fine adjustments to data. It is the place to look if something untoward is happening for which no other explanation is immediately apparent. The **score edit**, impressive as it looks, is the least useful platform for editing, as music notation cannot reflect the finer rhythmic details of performance. Its main function is for preparing sequenced material for printing out.

GROUP EDITING

With any of these methods it is usually possible to highlight a group of notes for mass editing. However, the screen size restricts the amount of data that can be shown, so sequencers offer a range of group editing facilities for entire tracks, patterns or bar-ranges. Some of these, such as **delete**, **copy** and **move**, are clear in meaning but the purpose of others may not be so obvious:

1. Pitch

Transpose moves the pitch of all selected notes or tracks up or down by a number of semitones. This will change the key of the music. Some sequencers provide more complex options such as **harmonic transpose** which also shifts patterns up or down, but makes further individual pitch adjustments to keep the music true to its original key signature. When transposing tracks, avoid changing the drum part unless you want it to sound on different instruments (see the Drum Tracks Fact Sheet on pages 40–41).

2. Velocity

Velocity data allows the sequencer to record the subtle dynamics of music. Synths respond by changing not only the relative loudness but also the attack and fundamental timbre of individual notes. Confusingly, MIDI also has a Volume controller for adjusting the amplification of a given channel. This is useful for balancing instruments in the mix, and for the special effect of creating a crescendo through a single note. It cannot alter the notes' original velocity levels, which are the only way to simulate the expressive range of a live player.

Set velocity will make all notes boringly equal in volume and attack at whatever level you request. **Adjust velocity** will add to (or subtract from) the existing levels of each note, leaving the original contours of the pattern intact. A **crescendo** transform will ramp velocity levels across a range of notes to make gradual dynamic changes.

3. Rhythm

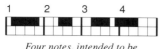

Four notes, intended to be quarter-notes, as recorded

Quantizing to quarters locks them to the nearest quarter-note beats

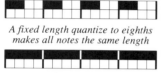

Quantizing to eighths pushes the second note to the wrong position

Imprecise rhythms can be nudged into place by **quantization**. This moves any rogue notes onto the nearest unit you specify – such as a sixteenth note (16), eighth (8), quarter (4), *etc.* Sequencers also provide for the temporary division of the beat into threes with a selection of triplet quantize values – 8T (or 12), 16T (or 24) and so on.

TIP There are two rules for successful quantization:

➡ the quantize value must not be greater than the shortest type of note in the music you are processing, otherwise these will get merged with their neighbours;

➡ none of the original recording must be out of time by more than 50% of the quantize value, or any such notes will get pushed onto the wrong beats. Most programs load with a default quantize value of 16 – make sure you change it if necessary.

Locking notes ruthlessly onto their correct beats can make some music sound robotic. If this proves hard to undo, a **humanize** option will attempt to restore the feel of a live performance by randomly moving notes slightly out of position – the reverse of quantizing, in fact. The problem can be avoided in the first place by using a **percentage quantize**: a 50% setting, for example, will move notes just halfway towards their correct places.

A fixed length quantize to eighths makes all notes the same length

A legato quantize removes any gaps between notes

A **note length** (or duration) quantize will make note lengths an exact multiple of the value you set without affecting their starting positions. **Fixed length** (or set duration) quantizing makes all notes the same length. Many sequencers offer a **legato** option which lengthens notes in order to close any gaps between them: it will not adjust overlapping notes, though. Finally, if you have played in a particularly good rhythm pattern, a **match** or **groove** quantize may allow you to line other parts up with it.

TIP You may find a facility called **auto quantize**. This will quantize your playing as you record, a function that can be useful for some rhythm parts. However, it will instantly obliterate any rhythmic subtlety before you have had a chance to listen back and make objective decisions about what is needed. Treat with caution!

Playback options

Sequencers offer many features designed to help you audition your work. These are often found on the "front page" (main screen) or in a track information box. It is usually possible to **solo**, **mute**, **loop**, **quantize** or **transpose** tracks. There may also be options to adjust track **velocity** levels and to **delay** (or advance) the output of one track in relation to the others. Most useful are the facilities to set a track's **program** number, **pan** position and **output volume** level. You can thus try a track on a variety of voices at different levels and positions in the mix.

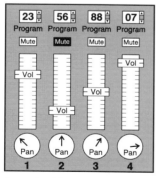

A graphic MIDI Mixer screen on the sequencer offers a particularly easy way of controlling playback settings for each track in the mix.

Many of these front page functions are designed to be "non-destructive" – they modify the MIDI output while leaving the original data in the sequence intact, making it possible to experiment with different values while the music is playing. Thus, a track transposed on the front page will still appear in its original key on the edit screens. Some sequencers provide graphic **MIDI mixers** for easy manipulation of playback data, enabling you to control the performance of your sequence from a single screen and store the settings for future use. However, remember that the Volume controls are just for balancing the mix and cannot replace careful editing of velocity levels for true dynamic variety.

This is also a good time to make fine decisions about tempo. The speeds we have given for the sequences reflect the tempo of the original recordings, although remember that live bands seldom keep as ruthlessly in time as the sequencer. A small increase of 1 or 2 bpm can give momentum when moving into a Chorus, while a more noticeable decrease may help to relax the last few bars of a ballad. Such subtle changes are very seldom notated in the music.

MIDI CONTROLLERS

In addition to recording and editing basic note information, you will almost certainly need to work with other MIDI instructions for controlling the synth. MIDI includes **controller** messages, such as modulation, pan and volume, and **channel** messages such as program change, pitch bend and aftertouch. Data for many of these can be recorded by the sequencer as you operate the synth's various controls, or it can be step-written directly into the sequence. It is particularly useful to be able to make program changes in mid track, especially in large-scale sequences where MIDI channels are at a premium. In this way, several voices that do not occur simultaneously can share the same track.

LIST:	Track 1, Channel 2			
Bar	Event	Val. 1	Val. 2	Value 3
1.1.0	Note	F 4	123	121
1.2.0	Note	E 4	105	146
1.3.0	Note	D# 4	88	133
1.4.0	Note	E 4	71	119
1.4.48	Prog	66	—	A. Sax
1.4.96	Contrl	10	127	Pan
2.1.0	Note	F 4	84	63
2.2.0	Note	E 4	78	67
2.3.0	Note	F 4	87	66
2.4.0	Contrl	7	120	Volume
3.1.0	Note	F 4	81	118
3.1.0	P_User	1	72	Tempo
3.2.0	Note	F# 4	77	116
3.2.96	Note	G 4	79	109

MIDI data on an Event Edit list can be added, changed or deleted. A controller message for panning the channel to 127 is selected, to place the alto sax voice on the far right.

Individual MIDI controller data and other events are usually edited alongside note information on an event edit list (see left), although they will not necessarily be displayed unless specially requested. This screen will usually also provide access to SysEx information. However, some MIDI messages, such as Pitch Bend, Modulation and Volume Controller generate so much data that it can be easier to view and edit such parameters on the graphic display incorporated into many Grid Edit screens (see page 55). Note that most synths implement only a selection of the wide range of control messages that are offered by sequencers.

While simple sequences may require little of this type of MIDI editing, familiarity with the procedures will be essential for sequencers with limited front-page settings or those which will not otherwise let you change program in mid track. It is also necessary for MIDI data to be written permanently into the sequence if you want to save your work as a Standard MIDI File (see below) since this format ignores most front-page settings. An option such as **freeze play parameters** or **normalize** may be available to make these settings permanent. Note that the SMF format will normally only store a single pattern per track. It will therefore be necessary, if you work in separate patterns, to edit each track into a single pattern (using a "glue" tool or a command such as "Arrange-to-pattern Copy"): check your sequencer manual.

SAVING & LOADING

· Files	
Save	
Save As	Save As ...
Load	Song
Delete	Track
Quit	Arrangement
	Drum Map
	MIDI File

A **files** menu will contain various options for saving and loading your work. Every manufacturer uses a different format for saving sequences to disk, thus ensuring that work saved in one sequencer will not load into one of a different make. A way around this annoying problem is mentioned below.

When saving a file, you should choose a name that will identify the contents for future reference: something like ATTHEHOP perhaps (many systems limit the name to eight characters). Sequences are normally saved as a **song file**, as this type will store all the musical data you have recorded. Many programs add a three-letter extension to the name, such as .SNG, .SON or .ALL.

It is usually possible to save selected parts of a recording, perhaps for merging into other pieces. An individual track (a bass part, for example) might be saved in a **track file**. A particular set-up of tracks, voices and other settings could be stored as an **arrangement** to form a template for other sequences, or the note numbers needed to trigger the instruments of a specific drum kit voice might be saved as a **drum map**.

Most sequencers give you this sort of variety when you select **load** (or open) to retrieve your work from disk and when you use the **save as...** function. Subsequently, you can use plain **save**, which will continue to store work with the name, and in the format, you have already chosen. To conserve disk space, check that you do not save unnecessary detail, such as any unwanted MIDI aftertouch data or even redundant sequences lurking in hidden windows.

TIP **Autosave** is a feature that will save files automatically at certain preset intervals. You may find, however, that the advantages of this are more than offset when autosave promptly preserves for posterity your latest and most mangled edit of a sequence, over-writing any more salvageable versions in the process. Much more useful is a facility to make **backup** versions of your files.

One final type of file, designed to get round the incompatibility problems of other formats, is the **Standard MIDI File**. This basic standard can be accepted by most sequencers, providing the computer's operating system can read the actual disk. This will allow your data to be played through other makes of sequencer, but remember that only track information is stored – most "front page" settings will be ignored and separate patterns need to be joined before saving. If given a choice, use a Type 1 MIDI file, since Type 0 puts all the data onto one track and Type 2 is often not implemented.

DISK ROUTINE

One of the most annoying and common occurrences is to lose valuable work that should be safe on disk. The following points will help avoid this danger:

➡ Save your work to disk *frequently* and keep back-ups of everything.

➡ Never allow anyone to use a disk in your equipment unless you know its origins and are certain that it is free of any computer virus. If you do regularly exchange disks with others, a virus-checking program will be essential.

➡ Have spare formatted disks ready to use when the current working disk is full if your computer doesn't allow you to format new disks once a program is loaded.

➡ Prevent accidental erasure by using the "write protect" notch on disks.

➡ Label disks clearly and store them away from equipment that generates magnetic fields, such as loudspeakers.

Sequencer program disks need special care. It is invariably quicker to run the program from a hard disk if your system has one. If not, always work from a *copy* of the original program and remove it from the disk drive as soon as it has loaded, unless your particular sequencer requires access to the disk while operating. If your program requires a security "dongle", never insert or remove it while the computer is running.

Using the Scores

The chapters in this book are arranged chronologically, but it does not follow that the earliest songs are the easiest to record. If you are new to sequencing, you may prefer to start with Sequence 9 or 12, where the layout is simple and the parts are easy to play. Some songs are built almost entirely from patterns which can be copied and in these chapters we have given layout diagrams to help. Sequences such as *Puppy Love* contain so much variation that we have printed every note in full score along with graphics to help with the more complex rhythms.

Most rock music uses guitar and bass guitar, which share the peculiar convention of being notated an octave higher than they sound to reduce the need for ledger lines above and below the stave. Synth guitar voices generally take this into account by already having the octave transposition pre-programmed, but listen carefully to these tracks and transpose them if they sound too high or too low.

Guitarists use many distinctive techniques, such as Hammer On and Pull Off, which are awkward to reproduce convincingly via MIDI. We suggest using pitch bend to create the sliding in pitch between notes that these essentially involve. Details of how to realise the special grey notation we have devised for this are shown on page 61.

Like guitars, high male vocal parts are also written in the treble clef, an octave above their sounding pitch. However, instrumental versions of these, especially lead parts, may well stand out better if recorded as written. Of course, our suggestions for voicing all tracks are intended only as a guide, and any decisions on transposition will have to depend on the sounds you finally select and how they sound in the mix.

The
Sequences

Selling Rebellion: the 1950s

Rock & Roll was born, so the story goes, in 1955 when Bill Haley's recording of Rock Around The Clock *was used on the film soundtrack of* Blackboard Jungle *and reached Number 1 in the US charts. Undeniably this was the year in which America's white youth finally caught on to the black tradition of Rhythm and Blues and claimed it for themselves. They were perhaps the first young generation to have money of their own to spend. No longer were white teenagers obliged to dance to the tunes that their parents enjoyed – vocalist-fronted big-band music (which had been stagnating since the war) and awful 'novelty' numbers such as* How Much Is That Doggie In The Window *(which was, incredibly, Number 1 for eight weeks in 1953). Rock & Roll was very simple music; a handful of basic chords played fast and loud with a good strong back-beat on the drums. As often as not, the lyrics were gibberish – they weren't important. This was music with attitude. It was fresh, exciting and a bit dangerous, and in next to no time it was everywhere.*

At The Hop

This hit by Danny and the Juniors was Number 1 for seven weeks in 1957-8 and shows how the rebellious aggression of early Rock & Roll was already being transformed into highly commercial dance music for jiving. Although the electric guitar had been around since the mid-thirties, its use was by no means universal as yet, and it appears neither in this song nor in *Sh-Boom* which follows. Both songs do, however, borrow from the black urban tradition of Doo-Wop (named after the 'doo-waah' often used by its backing singers). This style relied on a male vocal quartet (two tenors, baritone, bass) with 2nd tenor singing the lead and the other three forming a backing group. In *At the Hop* they are accompanied by the standard rhythm section of piano, string bass (not electric) and drums.

The music is printed on pages 20-21. The ¢ ('cut C') time signature indicates a version of $\frac{4}{4}$ with a feel of two half-note beats per bar – i.e. a strong pulse on the first and third quarters. The original was in the key of A major but it is given here in C for ease of playing. All tracks (except drums) could be transposed down 3 semitones, back to A, on completion.

ROCK & ROLL HARMONY

Rhythm and Blues, as its name suggests, was a hybrid style in which the energetic rhythms of jazz were superimposed on the previously slow-moving harmonies of the Blues. In much early Rock & Roll, this format was pushed to near-breakneck speeds but the familiar Blues chord patterns survived intact underneath. *At the Hop* uses the famous 12-bar pattern **C | C | C | C | F | F | C | C | G⁷ | F   C | C** to underpin both verse and chorus.

This blues harmony is one of the key features of the new style and, leaving aside issues of racial prejudice, it perplexed and enraged an older white generation which was used to popular music based on classical harmony. No longer was a sense of key defined and constantly re-inforced by means of V-I cadences (**G-C**, **D-G-C**, etc.) Instead, the prominence given to chord IV (**F** in this key) made the whole harmonic experience much more ambiguous, a dislocation which was further enhanced by the addition of 'blue' notes, usually flat 3 (here, E♭/D♯), flat 5 (G♭/F♯) and flat 7 (B♭). These were often used in close proximity to their natural versions (see bar 27) or even at the same time (bar 64 has E♮ in the treble and E♭ in the bass). No wonder Grandma hated it and fled back to the comfort of her beloved Bing Crosby albums!

DRUMS

The various two-bar drum patterns are all typical of early Rock & Roll, with the snare on beats two and four giving the traditional 'back beat' feel:

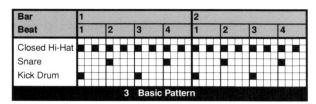

Enter these two bars first using light, dry sounds – drums were not over-prominent in the mix of recordings made in the '50s. Make four copies of the pattern and edit into these the following variations for different parts of the song:

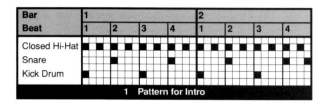

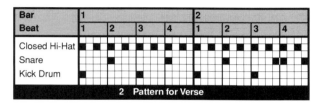

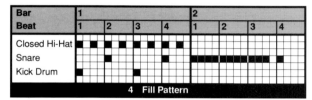

Now assemble the complete track, copying these patterns out in the order printed under the bass part of the score – notice that the drums do not begin until bar 3, after which you need four sets of Pattern 1, six of Pattern 2, and so on. You could try varying the fill patterns when they are used later in the song. For a final touch of authenticity, add handclaps on beats two and four throughout bars 63–74.

TIP Instead of laboriously making individual copies of each pattern, see if your sequencer will enable you to enter a pattern once and then to specify how many times you want it played. If it allows these repeats to be made as **ghost copies**, they should take up less computer memory space and less room on disk.

BASS

All 74 bars can be played in as printed – use a string bass (e.g. **pizz bass**) if possible, as the bass guitar was not in general use at this time. It is in quarter notes throughout (a pattern known as 'walking bass') so step writing is a practical option. Music for the bass sounds an octave lower than written – this should happen automatically from the synth if you select a bass-type voice. The part is doubled throughout by the piano left hand, at the printed pitch, so make a copy of the bass track (a 'ghost copy' would again be ideal) and assign to a rough-sounding **piano** voice.

PIANO

For most of the song the piano right hand plays bars of hammered eighth-notes using just the four chord patterns below. Record each of the bars as a separate one-bar pattern and then copy out, following the chord letters printed over the bass part in the score – six bars of **C** at the start, then 2 of **Am** (A minor), and so on. Once bars 15–26 have been assembled for the verse, they can be directly copied to form the chorus (bars 27–38), since both sections use the same 12-bar blues pattern.

TIP If you find playing chords tricky they could be step written. Alternatively, your sequencer may have a facility for **cycle recording**. If so, you can set up a one-bar loop and add each layer separately as the bar cycles round and round.

The piano right-hand part in bars 63–74 will need to be recorded in full – the *8ve* symbol indicates that the whole section needs to be transposed up by an octave (12 semitones). Velocity levels can be higher for this solo, but give yourself headroom for a final wild *crescendo* to mark the return of the verse in bars 73–74.

Just as the drum fills can be varied in later repeats, so the piano part can be elaborated – preferably in bars when the solo has a silence to avoid masking the tune. Here are some ideas from the original record that can be used to replace the piano chords in the bars shown during later playings of the Chorus. These one-bar patterns should also be transposed up by an octave so they stand out well in the mix:

BVOX

This part was originally sung by a backing vocal group (*vox* is Latin for voice), mainly to single syllables such as 'hop' and 'aah'. Synth sounds such as **choir** and **voices** are likely to lack the incisive attack needed – try **trumpet** or **brass** instead.

The bvox contribution to the Intro consists of slow arpeggios: notice that you have to hold each note down until the very end of the two-bar pattern. After this, aim for crisp playing of eighth notes and *staccato* quarters to contrast with longer notes elsewhere. Emphasize the jazzy use of syncopation at the end of bars 15, 17, etc. Once again, the second verse could be varied by playing just one 8-beat chord in each pair of bars, instead of using the rhythms printed for verse one.

SOLO

Beat	1	2	3	4
E 4				
D# 4				
D 4				
C# 4				
C 4				

Although originally sung, this part should work well voiced for **sax** – the saxophone was often used in early Rock & Roll bands. Even if you quantize all the other tracks, try to leave a little rhythmic freedom in this part. The ornament in bar 62 (called a 'crushed note' or *acciaccatura*) should sound just before the second beat and must be as short as possible (see left).

GETTING IT TOGETHER

In the score overleaf, the music runs straight through from the start to bar 38, giving an Intro, Verse and Chorus. There is then a repeat from bar 15 to give a second Verse and Chorus, forming bars 39–62. The bracketed '1.' above bar 38 indicates music that is required for the first playing only. When you make the copies for the repeat this will become bar 62 and will need the changes in the bass and solo parts shown in the 'second time bar', printed in the score with a bracketed '2.'. At this stage, make any of the changes suggested above to vary the music for the second verse. Now read on!

The next section (the Release, bars 63–74) is printed in full. Notice that the solo and bvox are silent here. The instruction **Dal Segno** means 'from the sign' (𝄋) – so next copy just bars 15–26 to make Verse 3, filling bars 75–86. A repeat of bars 39–62 forms Verse 4 and a final Chorus (making bars 87–110 of the sequence). Lastly, the instruction in bar 62 indicates that an ending should be made by repeating bars 5–13 to give bars 111–119. Copy from the ⊕ sign in bar 5 to the word *fine* ('finish') in bar 13 and delete everything after the first note of bar 13 to give a crisp end. Confused? Here is a diagram of the complete layout:

Bars	1–14	15–26	27–38	39–50	51–62	63–74	75–86	87–98	99–110	111–119
Section	Intro	Verse 1	Chorus	Verse 2	Chorus	Release	Verse 3	Verse 4	Chorus	Coda
Editing Instructions	Record as printed			Copy of 15–38 (+ changes in bar 62)		Record as printed	Copy of 15–26	Copy of 39–62		Copy of 5–13

Doo-Wop and the Swing Tradition

The straight eighth notes of Rock & Roll never completely obliterated the swing rhythms of the big band era, which continued to be used for slower ballads, especially in Doo-Wop. This style developed in the black ghettos of New York in the decade up to 1955 and featured a lead singer shadowed by backing vocalists in close harmony – as often as not on the syllables "Doo-waa" (hence the name). The all-male vocal line-up used by Doo-Wop later became a feature of many '60s groups.

Sh-Boom was a Number 1 hit in 1957 for a Canadian vocal group, The Crewcuts, although it was actually a cover of a 1954 New York original by The Chords – thus continuing an established pattern of white versions of black music stealing the market. Swing rhythms predominate and the vocal is punctuated by brass fills (another legacy of big band music). Unlike *At The Hop*, the harmony is far removed from the blues: the Middle Eight uses a classic 'cycle of fifths' – a chain of chords a fifth apart – with the progression **E^7–A^7–D^7–G^7** leading back to **C** for the second verse.

SEQUENCING SWING

In jazz, the term 'swing' is used to denote a rhythmic *feel*, almost an attitude to the music, which is hard to quantify exactly and may even vary slightly from song to song. In general terms, swing rhythms divide each beat into three rather than two, as shown in the drum grids below. On the sequencer, the simplest way to achieve this is to use a $\frac{12}{8}$ time signature which will allow eighth-notes to be written or quantised into their correct positions. However, be aware that the speed of 130bpm in the score refers to dotted quarter beats – you may need to increase this by 50% if your sequencer always bases its pulse on straight quarter notes. You should use a normal 8 quantize – don't be misled by the 8T option, which is for producing swing-type rhythms in quarter-note time signatures such as $\frac{4}{4}$.

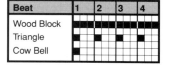

TIP Sequencer metronome beats in $\frac{12}{8}$ can be hard to follow because most persist in beeping all 12 eighth notes without highlighting the four main beats, making it difficult to work out where you are in the bar. If so, use drum sounds to create your own $\frac{12}{8}$ metronome, such as the one-bar repeating pattern shown left. Save this for future use.

Experienced sequencer users may wish to investigate the various quantise options such as **Groove** and **Iterative** which allow fine adjustments to the rhythmic template and are useful if you want to create a swing feel which is slightly more urgent or laid-back than plain old $\frac{12}{8}$.

Recording the Sequence

DRUMS

Only hi-hat cymbal is needed in this song. Two one-bar patterns will suffice for the whole sequence except for one special pattern needed at the **cross-rhythm** in bar 25. Here, the lolloping effect elsewhere of four groups of three per bar is replaced by six even groups of two. You won't need a new time signature, but take care if quantizing this bar and make sure that bvox and bass tracks line up when you get to them.

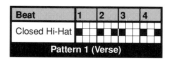

Pattern 1 (Verse)

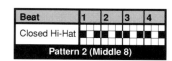

Pattern 2 (Middle 8)

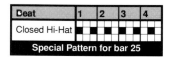

Special Pattern for bar 25

Use pattern 1 in bars 2–21 and in the Coda (36–44). Delete all notes after the first in bar 44. Use pattern 2 for the Middle 8 (22–29) and then replace bar 25 with the special cross-rhythm pattern above. The empty bars (30-35) will eventually be filled by a partial repeat of the Verse. Do this at the end as a global cut-and-paste job on all tracks.

BASS

Sh-Boom has an upbeat start – the bass plays a preliminary eighth to kick the song into life – leaving other tracks to begin in bar 2. From here to bar 19, however, the bass repeats the same two-bar pattern (B) which can be copied. The part for the Middle 8 and Coda is fully written out. As with *At The Hop*, use a **plucked string bass** rather than electric bass if you are interested in authenticity, and quantize as required to match the hi-hat.

PIANO

The two-bar pattern (A) in bars 2–3 is repeated until the end of bar 19. It can also be used again in the Coda, filling bars 38–43. The piano is not needed in the Middle 8, a convention in many songs which traditionally used a thinned-down rhythm section at this point.

BVOX AND SOLO

Record as written throughout. The bvox will probably work best on a **soft brass** voice although you may wish to experiment with some of your synth's vocal 'ooh-aah' options for the Middle 8. The solo can go on **clarinet**, **vibes**, or any lyrical voice that your synth does well. Or try singing it karaoke-style – we've printed the words!

FILLS

Record the following two-bar fills on muted trumpet and drop into the bars shown:

TIP Fill 3 uses some extensive syncopation in which the last five chords are played an eighth ahead of the beat. This would be second nature to a big-band horn section but if you find it tricky to record, play *with* the beat and then shift the chords back when editing.

OPTIONAL SAX

The Crewcuts' version of *Sh-Boom* has baritone sax doubling the bass part at the beginning and end. Make a copy of the bass track from the start to the first note of bar 6 and a similar copy of 38–44. Voice for the roughest-sounding **sax** voice you have. It may need to be transposed down an octave.

LAYOUT

As mentioned earlier, all tracks will need a copy of bars 6–11 inserted into 30–35 to form the repeat of the Verse. Note that 38–39 can also be copied to form the double repeat in the Coda. Here is an overview of the layout, omitting fills, drums and sax:

Bars	1–5	6–19	20–21	22–29	30–35	36–44
Section	Intro	Verse 1		Middle 8	Verse 2 (shortened)	Coda
Editing Instructions	Record as printed: piano and bass repeat patterns A and B throuhout bars 2–19			Record as printed	Copy of 6–11	Record as printed (38-39 can be copied)

The original song was in E♭ major, so transpose all tracks except hi-hat up three semitones. The Crewcuts' recording doesn't actually end at this point – after five beats of silence there is a loud solo G for timp (beat 2 of bar 45)which, by means of a pedal, is made to swoop up towards C through the rest of the bar like a musical trampoline. This heralds a series of varied repeats of all the previous material. A "stop bar" like this is a classic device for a surprise continuation of a song after everyone thinks it is finished.

Sh-Boom (Life Could Be A Dream)

Rock & Roll

Larry Williams was a classic 50s Rocker along the lines of that other great 'sock-it-to-'em' specialist, Little Richard. He wrote his own material, unlike Elvis Presley and many other contemporaries, and seems to have been somewhat preoccupied with girls' names. His first 1957 hit was a song called Short Fat Fannie *and the following year saw* Dizzy Miss Lizzy, *which was later covered by the Beatles.* Bony Moronie *(also from 1957) has many similarities with* At The Hop – *energetic pounding from the piano and a 12-bar blues harmony scheme which is here stretched over 24 bars with some neat shuffling of chords under the Chorus. However, in its rough directness,* Bony Moronie *is much more of a solo singer's number, and the rhythm section is padded out with saxophone and electric guitar to make up for the lack of backing vocals. Williams was also famous as a whistler and so this sequence offers a rare opportunity to make authentic use of one of the synth's more arcane voices.*

LAYOUT

The song (printed on pages 28–29) consists of an Intro followed by four repeats of verse and chorus. The first two of these are sung, the third is a sax solo and the fourth consists of a whistled version of the tune, leading to either a fade-out or a manufactured ending as you prefer. The layout diagram below will help you to assemble the song.

Bars	1–5	6–21	22–29	30–45	46–53	54–69	70–77	78–93	94–101
Section	Intro	Verse 1	Chorus	Verse 2	Chorus	Verse 3	Chorus	Verse 4	Chorus
Editing Instructions	Record as printed			Copy of bars 6–29		Copy of bars 6–29 plus sax solo and brass fills		Copy of bars 6–29 + fills (see text for ending)	

DRUMS

Although you may want to elaborate them on the repeats, two basic patterns will again suffice for virtually the whole song – a four-bar pattern that is used for most of the song and a single bar that is repeated in the first half of the Chorus:

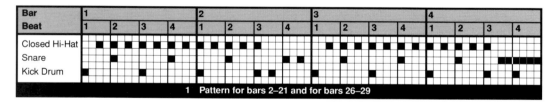

1 Pattern for bars 2–21 and for bars 26–29

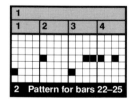

2 Pattern for bars 22–25

Notice how the snare drum springs into life with 16th notes at the end of the four-bar pattern, propelling the music into the next phrase. The snare is also used to kick-start the song with the rhythm shown left, which is used in bar 1 only.

BASS

Record as written, copying patterns where appropriate. Notice that the part contains more syncopation than the straight walking quarters found in *At The Hop*. As mentioned earlier, bass parts (and guitar parts in general) are usually written an octave higher than their sounding pitch to prevent the need for too many ledger lines beneath the stave when the actual pitches get very low. A small figure 8 is sometimes printed under the clef as a reminder of this transposition. Synth bass voices mostly come ready-transposed so that the user similarly does not keep running out of keyboard at the bottom end. Be aware of this when voicing, however, and make any necessary transposition from the sequencer if your ear tells you things are not right.

PIANO

The 2-bar chord patterns can be recorded and copied out as with previous sequences. At the very start, and leading into each repeat, is another characteristic feature of early Rock & Roll piano playing – the *glissando*. This is a very rapid scale produced by sweeping the thumbnail down the white notes of the keyboard. It is indicated in the

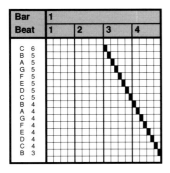

Bar	1			
Beat	1	2	3	4

music by the starting note of the scale, the abbreviation *gliss.* and a line to show the downward direction. The effect sounds (and looks) great live; on the sequencer it is probably easiest to step-write a white note scale in thirty-second notes starting on the third beat of bar 1. Begin on C6 (the top note on most five-octave synth keyboards) and 16 notes later you should be down on B3, comfortably placed to start the chords in bar 2 (see left). Copy bar 1 and overlay it onto bars 29, 53 and 77 for the repeats. Use B naturals in the *glissando* – a live player would find it physically impossible to incorporate the B flats indicated by the key signature. Not that the sequencer always has to mimic live performance. You could, for instance, experiment with a chromatic *glissando* – something no pianist could manage at this speed. For this you would need to include all notes, white and black.

ELECTRIC GUITAR

Caution is needed when sequencing guitar parts since they are also printed an octave higher than they sound, just like the bass but using a treble clef. Many synth guitar voices already have this octave transposition programmed into the preset. Appropriate voices, such as **pick guitar**, may respond best in this kind of material if the notes are played *staccato*. To provide variety in Verse 4, the guitar can be used to play the fills that were given to brass in Verse 3 – this may be better than a fourth repeat of the printed guitar patterns.

SAX

The original song needed two saxophones to play the chords in the chorus. There is also a full-scale solo for one of the players in verse 3 – this is printed on page 30.

TIP If you want to reproduce the effect of two players in the verses, make a copy of the track (a 'ghost' copy will conserve memory) and set it to a different channel but still voiced for **sax**. Then delay this copy fractionally so that the ear recognizes the difference – similar to the more randomized **chorus** effect available on many synths.

VOCAL

Record as written, using an up-front, decisive voice such as **trumpet**. This is repeated for Verses 2 and 4 but not Verse 3, which has the sax solo instead. On the record, the final verse is whistled – try a suitably nonchalant sound for Verse 4 (from bar 78).

BRASS FILLS

The following fills accompany the sax solo in Verse 3 (bars 54-77) and need a piercingly bright brass voice such as **muted trumpet**. It is important that the notes are detached and accurate in length, since the precise releasing of such chords can add much to the rhythmic impetus. Try a length-size quantise if they need tidying. Copy the patterns into bars 78–101 on the guitar track if you want to use them to replace the existing guitar part in Verse 4.

ENDING

Once you have assembled the sequence as shown on the layout diagram, it can be finished in one of two ways. Either fade to nothing, starting at the Chorus in Verse 4 (bar 94) or do the following:

➡ Cut all tracks after the final eighth in bar 100
➡ Edit the bass to double the sax in this bar (i.e. move the D back by an eighth)
➡ Delete the snare's last sixteenth in bar 100 of the drum track.

SAX SOLO

In bars 54–77 (Verse 3 and its Chorus) the vocals are silent and neither of the printed sax patterns is used. Instead, there is the following raunchy solo. This will almost certainly need to be input very slowly but is well worth the effort – it will make all the difference at the point where the song might otherwise lose energy on its third repetition. It is also revealing to see how the use of altered and extra notes can make even a simple three-chord blues pattern sound rich and colourful.

TIP Keep the crushed notes very short (no more than a thirty-second at this tempo) and positioned about a thirty-second ahead of their following notes. If you record this solo live and at a very slow speed, make sure that the crushed notes are substantial enough not to disappear at the playback tempo of 180 bpm.

Experienced players may want to experiment with modulation on some longer notes. The occasional use of pitch bend will also make the solo sound more authentic. Both these topics are explored in detail later in the book.

Verse 3

Chorus

General MIDI

If you have ever tried playing a disk of your sequences on a friend's system, you may well have been faced with the embarrassment of hearing all the voicings you carefully set up to suit your own synth play back on entirely the wrong sounds – brilliant brass stabs turned into soggy string chords and drum parts replaced by wildly discordant bass sounds. This is because MIDI uses numbers to trigger voices: numbers which different manufacturers may have assigned to entirely different types of sounds on their own equipment.

General MIDI System Level 1 ('GM') is a system designed to offer some degree of standardization by assigning similar types of sound to MIDI program numbers 1–128. Thus, voice number 1 should always trigger a piano sound (although on sequencers that use the range 0–127 you will have to add 1 each time). Synths from any manufacturer that claim to be GM (or 'GS', an extension of the system, used by Roland) should replay pre-voiced sequences in an at least recognizable fashion. GM also lays down other specifications for synths, such as a minimum of 24-note polyphony, velocity sensitivity, minimum controller implementation, common pitch standards, and ability to receive on all 16 MIDI channels with drums on channel 10. It also assigns certain notes on the keyboard to specific drum sounds within the kit – these are given later, in the Drum Tracks Fact Sheet, on page 40.

We have sometimes used GM sound descriptions in this book – although there is no need to worry if you don't have a GM synth as we have described the type of voice needed for each track so you can always select your own most appropriate sounds. Even if you do have a GM synth, always use your ears rather than your eyes to decide on the voice to use as there can be noticeable differences between supposedly similar sounds – one manufacturer's trumpet can be fat and jazzy, while another's might be thin and penetrating. There can also be small differences in the precise voice names given below, which are grouped into GM's 16 not entirely logical categories.

Piano
1 Acoustic Grand Piano
2 Bright Acoustic Piano
3 Electric Grand Piano
4 Honky Tonk Piano
5 Electric Piano 1
6 Electric Piano 2
7 Harpsichord
8 Clavi

Chromatic Percussion
9 Celesta
10 Glockenspiel
11 Music Box
12 Vibraphone
13 Marimba
14 Xylophone
15 Tubular Bells
16 Dulcimer

Organ
17 Drawbar Organ
18 Percussive Organ
19 Rock Organ
20 Church Organ
21 Reed Organ
22 Accordion
23 Harmonica
24 Tango Accordion

Guitar
25 Acoustic Guitar (nylon)
26 Acoustic Guitar (steel)
27 Electric Guitar (jazz)
28 Electric Guitar (clean)
29 Electric Guitar (muted)
30 Overdriven Guitar
31 Distortion Guitar
32 Guitar Harmonics

Bass
33 Acoustic Bass
34 Electric Bass (fingered)
35 Electric Bass (picked)
36 Fretless Bass
37 Slap Bass 1
38 Slap Bass 2
39 Synth Bass 1
40 Synth Bass 2

Strings
41 Violin
42 Viola
43 Cello
44 Double Bass
45 Tremolo Strings
46 Pizzicato Strings
47 Orchestral Harp
48 Timpani

Ensemble
49 String Ensemble 1
50 String Ensemble 2
51 Synth Strings 1
52 Synth Strings 2
53 Choir Aahs
54 Voice Oohs
55 Synth Voice
56 Orchestral Hit

Brass
57 Trumpet
58 Trombone
59 Tuba
60 Muted Trumpet
61 French Horn
62 Brass Section
63 Synth Brass 1
64 Synth Brass 2

Reed
65 Soprano Sax
66 Alto Sax
67 Tenor Sax
68 Baritone Sax
69 Oboe
70 English Horn
71 Bassoon
72 Clarinet

Pipe
73 Piccolo
74 Flute
75 Recorder
76 Pan Flute
77 Blown Bottle
78 Shakuhachi
79 Whistle
80 Ocarina

Synth Lead
81 Square Wave
82 Sawtooth Wave
83 Calliope
84 Chiff
85 Charang
86 Voice
87 Fifths
88 Bass & Lead

Synth Pad
89 New Age
90 Warm Pad
91 Polysynth
92 Choir Pad
93 Bowed Pad
94 Metallic
95 Halo Pad
96 Sweep Pad

Synth FX
97 Rain
98 Soundtrack
99 Crystal
100 Atmosphere
101 Brightness
102 Goblins
103 Echoes
104 Sci-Fi

Ethnic
105 Sitar
106 Banjo
107 Shamisen
108 Koto
109 Kalimba
110 Bagpipes
111 Fiddle
112 Shanai

Percussive
113 Tinkle Bell
114 Agogo
115 Steel Drums
116 Wood Block
117 Taiko Drum
118 Melodic Drum
119 Synth Drum
120 Reverse Cymbal

Sound FX
121 Guitar Fret Noise
122 Breath Noise
123 Seashore
124 Bird Tweet
125 Telephone Ring
126 Helicopter
127 Applause
128 Gun Shot

Sequence 4

The Teen Idol and Soft Rock

Sex appeal sells records, and the world of pop is littered with the burnt-out careers of photogenic boys (and a few girls) who were once the focus of a million teenage fantasies. A few, like Neil Sedaka and the subject of this chapter, Paul Anka, managed to survive the leap into adulthood mainly because they were also gifted songwriters. For most of the others, though, the bubble of fame burst when the teenybopper army transferred its fickle affections to the latest baby-faced arrival. Who now remembers David Cassidy or the Bay City Rollers?

Puppy Love

Puppy Love is a perfect example of the 'Middle-of-the-Road' (MOR) style that has always existed alongside harder rock music – yearningly romantic and richly scored (notice the typical soaring string part). Although a teeny-song, later made famous again by Donny Osmond, it was also inoffensive enough not to frighten the parents of the young audience whose pocket money the record companies were after.

The style has more in common with *Sh-Boom* than with either of the other previous songs. The slow swing rhythm and the format of 8-bar verses with chords based on falling fifths date back to an earlier era. Similarly, the drum part is just a soft shuffle, very much in the background. Paul Anka's voice is closely miked on the original recording, and treated to a wash of reverberation – a technique that had also been successful for Elvis Presley. This, combined with frequent sobs on the line "help me please", gives *Puppy Love* the sort of harrowing emotional appeal which made a star of Johnnie Ray, the 'Nabob of Sob'.

The lush orchestral scoring marks a resurgence of the 'professional' song writer/ arranger. Anka was particularly precocious – his first hit, *Diana* (1957) was written when he was just 16. He has subsequently produced material which has been taken up by many leading MOR practitioners, most notably Frank Sinatra with *My Way*.

Recording the Sequence

Puppy Love is printed here in full to show how the orchestration varies from verse to verse. This is particularly evident in the strings and bvox parts, but many sections of other tracks are repeated and can be copied. The new key signature at the start of Verse 4 indicates a shift from G major to A♭. Transposition up a semitone is a classic device used by arrangers to give the last verse of a song a new lease of life.

DRUMS

The drum patterns have been printed as part of the score throughout the song as there are small but significant variations. This incidentally illustrates one of those confusing aspects of music notation – proportional spacing. Compare the drum grids in bars 19 and 20 and you will see how much printed music distorts the rhythmic uniformity of the sequencer's grid edit display. On the record, most of the part is played on a snare drum, but using wire brushes instead of sticks – a gentle, unpercussive sound that can be reasonably imitated by **shaker** or **maracas** on most synths. The ✗ symbol in this part is a shorthand indication that the previous bar should be repeated.

TIP The drums sign off with a tiny flourish in bar 45. Make sure the other parts shut down in time for this to register.

BASS AND GUITAR

By the end of the 50s the acoustic string bass had mainly been replaced in pop music by the more incisive (and potentially louder) **bass guitar**. The guitar part in this song was originally played on a steel guitar ("Hawaiian guitar"). It is a quite different sound from the 12-string guitar used by folk singers, often included as a synth voice under the name 'steel guitar' because it uses steel (rather than nylon) strings. A soft **acoustic guitar** or **clean electric guitar** is likely to be better in this case. Unlike other guitarists, players of the steel guitar do not finger the strings with their left hand to produce different pitches but use instead a small steel tube to slide up and down the fingerboard. This produces a distinctive glide (*portamento*) from chord to chord. Keen sequencers may wish to experiment with portamento controller or pitch bend to reproduce the slide between the longer chords in verse 1, where the instrument is most noticeable.

STRINGS

This is the kind of sustained, high part which will bring the best out of your synth string voices. It was recorded using an entire string section, not just violins, to produce a rich sound in octaves for much of the song. The main line should sound an octave higher than printed throughout (as indicated by the *8va* sign at the start). However, if you don't have a **string ensemble** voice (GM 49) you may want to duplicate the part an octave lower (at the written pitch) for the Intro, and from Verse 3 onwards, to reproduce the lower sound of violas and cellos in the texture. Notice that the material in bars 12–17 is not used in Verse 1. Fast moving scales are one of the most distinctive features of this kind of string writing. Some of these use rather tricky rhythms – help with recording these is given at the foot of this page.

GLOCKENSPIEL

The glockenspiel has tuned metal bars, unlike the xylophone, which is made of wood. It is a common feature of this kind of orchestration, adding brightness to the texture and highlighting melodies. GM 10 is assigned to a **glockenspiel** voice. Alternatively you could use **vibes** (which also have metal bars), but you may need to transpose the music up by at least one octave to get the right type of bell-like sound.

BVOX

For most of the song, the group of backing vocalists sings "ooh" or "aah". It is quite a large group – Verse 2 has the existing part on Track 2 as well as an additional line which will need to be copied from the strings track (at the written pitch) in bars 12–17. Use a **choir** voice or a suitably soft brass sound.

SOLO

The words are printed, in case you want to sing along, karaoke-style. Otherwise try a soft **oboe** or **pan flute** voice. Paul Anka is much freer in his rhythm than the notation would suggest, generally locking onto only the main beats. Imagine how you would sing the part when recording it and don't over-quantize.

TRIPLETS, DUPLETS AND TUPLETS

The song is launched with a long scale for strings. This is printed in 16th notes, but they are grouped in threes, with the figure *3* above each group. These are **triplets** – three notes that have to be compressed into the space normally occupied by two. Such triplets can be step written using the '16T' resolution specially provided by sequencers for this purpose. Take care with the later ones in bars 19 and 29 where the scales include a pair of normal 16th notes alongside the triplets – we have shown the position of notes relative to beats on grids in these bars.

The opposite of the triplet is the **duplet** – two notes that have to be expanded into the space normally occupied by three. Five sets of duplets occur in the last line of the song. If recording these is problematic, try step writing using a 'dotted 8' resolution.

Other irregular divisions of the beat, quadruplets, quintuplets, sextuplets, and so on, are generally referred to as **tuplets**. They follow the same principle of grouping the notes together under a number printed in italic type which shows the total number of notes to be fitted into the space available. Some mathematical calculation can be needed with the more complex groupings in order to work out whether compression or expansion of notes is needed! To help, we have included further grids to use as templates for the vocal part in bar 5 (a quadruplet) and the strings in bar 33 (an octuplet). The precise positions and lengths of these notes are likely to need manual adjustment when editing to ensure they are regularly spaced and *legato*.

TIP Don't spoil the effect of your labours by later quantizing these bars accidentally.

Puppy Love

105 bpm

Words and music by Paul Anka

Intro

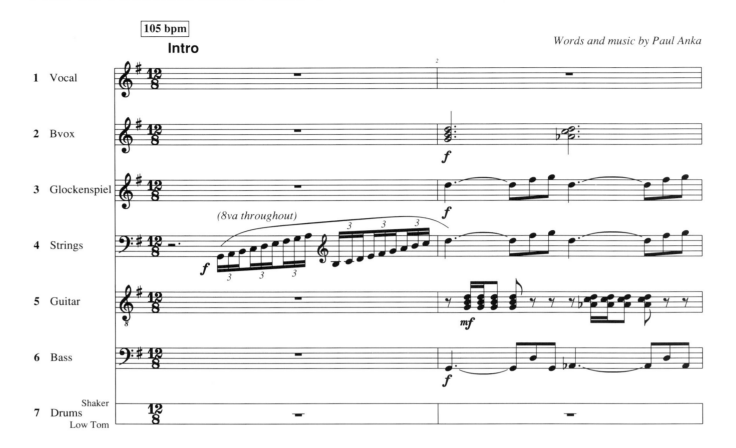

1 Vocal
2 Bvox
3 Glockenspiel
4 Strings *(8va throughout)*
5 Guitar
6 Bass
7 Drums — Shaker / Low Tom

Vocal rhythm:

Verses 1 and 2

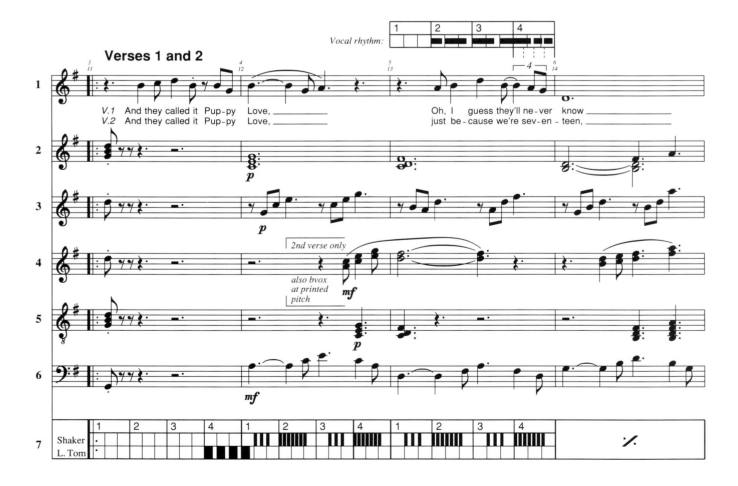

V.1 And they called it Pup-py Love, _____ Oh, I guess they'll ne-ver know _____
V.2 And they called it Pup-py Love, _____ just be-cause we're sev-en-teen, _____

2nd verse only

also bvox at printed pitch

7 Shaker / L. Tom

how a young heart   real-ly feels, ___   and __ why I ___ love her   so. ___
Tell them all it ___   is-n't fair ___   to take a - way my ___ on-ly   dream. ___

(Both verses)

Bridge

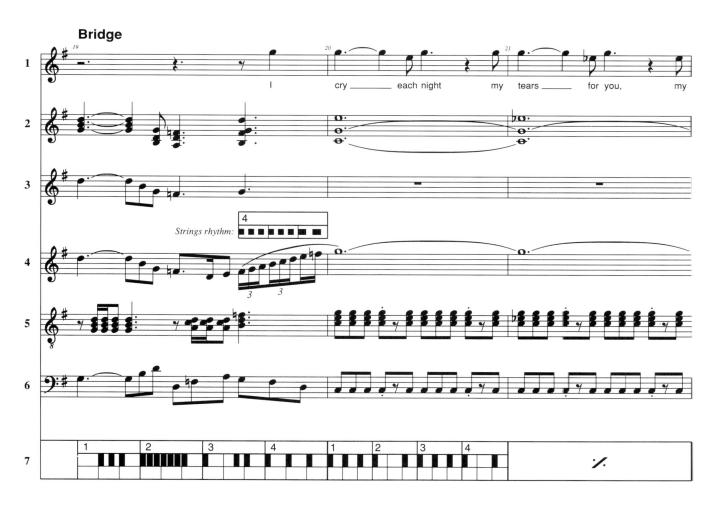

I   cry ___ each night   my   tears ___ for you,   my

Strings rhythm:

tears _____ are all _____ in vain. _____ I'll hope and I'll pray that __

may - be some day __ you'll be back in my arms once a - gain. _____

(you'll be back in my arms, you'll be back in my arms once a -

Verse 3

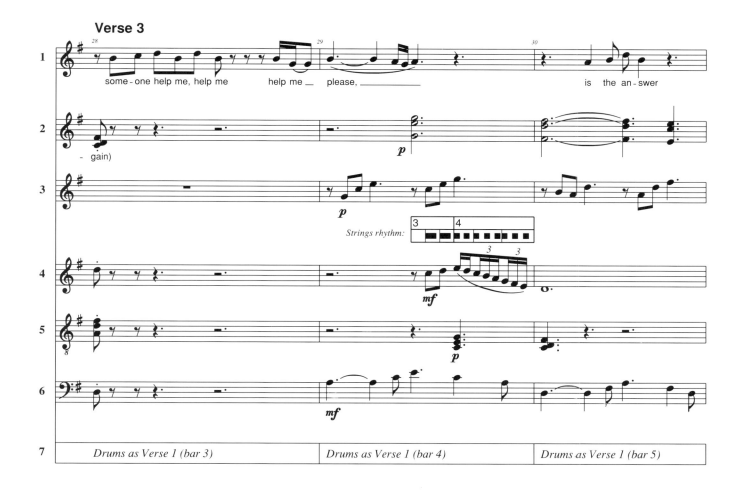

some-one help me, help me   help me __ please, ____   is the an-swer
- gain)

up a-bove? ____   How can I, oh, how can I   tell   them ____

Verse 4

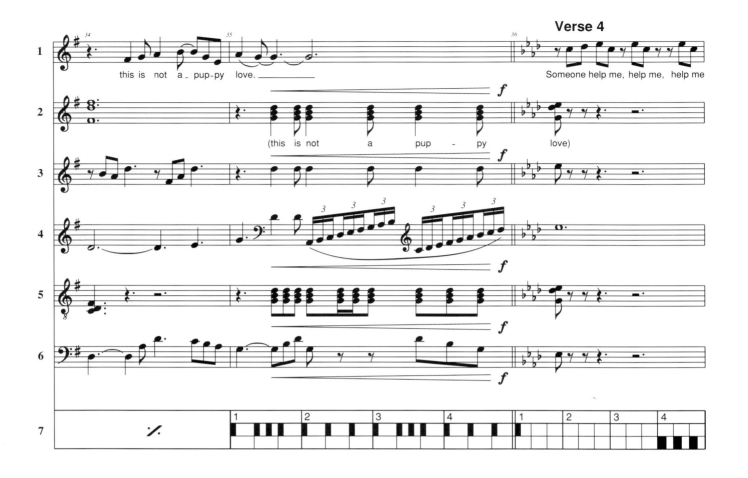

this is not a_ pup-py love. _____

(this is not a pup - py love)

Someone help me, help me, help me

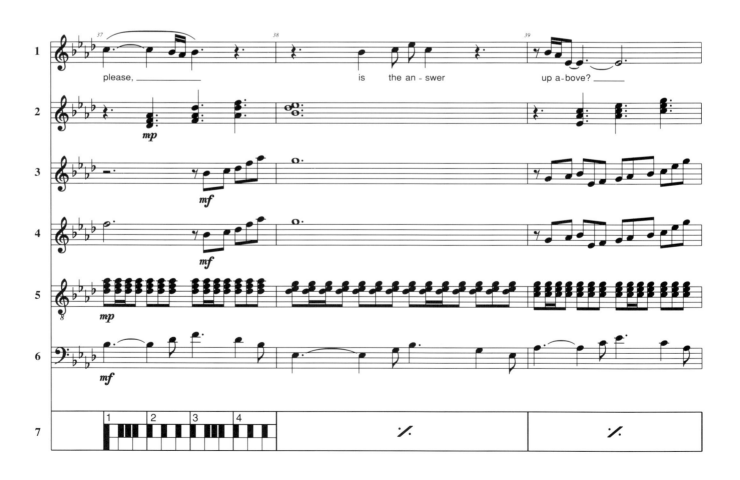

please, _____

is the an - swer

up a-bove? _____

Drum Tracks

DRUM KIT

A drum kit, which lies at the heart of all rock music, normally includes at least the following instruments:

> **kick drum** (sometimes called a bass drum)
> **snare drum**
> **hi-hat cymbals** (can be played 'open' or 'closed')
> **crash cymbal**
> **tom-toms** (2 or 3, of different sizes)

In a typical early rock 'n' roll drum pattern, the kick drum lays down the main beats (beats 1 and 3), the snare emphasises the back beats (2 and 4), the hi-hat decorates the rhythm with eighth notes (eight to a bar). The toms and crash cymbal are often used to elaborate this basic pattern with a 'fill' at the ends of lines in the song:

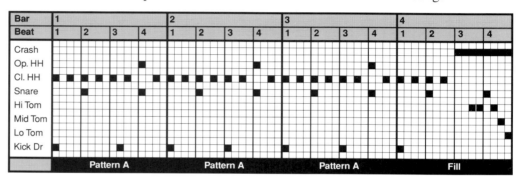

This type of rhythm grid, similar to that found on drum machines, has been used for many of the drum patterns in this book. Most sequencers offer a similar facility, called a Drum Edit Screen, on which you can enter the notes you need by clicking on the grid with a mouse. Drummers who read music would be familiar with seeing the above pattern written in this rather more compact, if complicated, type of notation :

NOTATION

The kick drum part is written at the bottom of the stave, with stems pointing downwards and rests printed where needed – notice that there is seldom room to include rests for the other instruments on the stave. The snare is usually written in the third space, with stems pointing either up or down. The x-headed notes at the top are for hi-hat cymbals – normally struck with their two plates closed to produce a dry sound (**closed hi-hat**). The circle around some of the note heads indicates that the drummer should release the foot pedal which opens the plates to give a brighter sound (**open hi-hat**). These two sounds will have separate notes on a synth's drum list.

Finally, other instruments are fitted around these – the three tom-toms (abbreviated TT) in the remaining spaces, with the highest at the top. Other cymbals, such as the crash, usually share the hi-hat position but are identified individually. Because the sound of a crash cymbal can last longer than most other percussion sounds, the x-head is often replaced by a diamond-shaped note head for lengths of two beats or more.

The precise layout of drum staves can vary, but a key is often given at the start of the piece, especially when unusual instruments are involved.

DRUM MAPPING

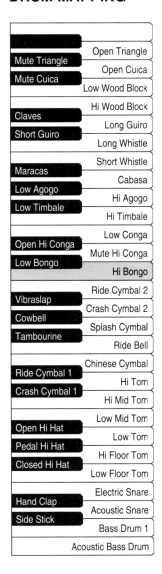

	Open Triangle
Mute Triangle	
	Open Cuica
Mute Cuica	
	Low Wood Block
	Hi Wood Block
Claves	
	Long Guiro
Short Guiro	
	Long Whistle
	Short Whistle
Maracas	
	Cabasa
Low Agogo	
	Hi Agogo
Low Timbale	
	Hi Timbale
	Low Conga
Open Hi Conga	
	Mute Hi Conga
Low Bongo	
	Hi Bongo
	Ride Cymbal 2
Vibraslap	
	Crash Cymbal 2
Cowbell	
	Splash Cymbal
Tambourine	
	Ride Bell
	Chinese Cymbal
Ride Cymbal 1	
	Hi Tom
Crash Cymbal 1	
	Hi Mid Tom
	Low Mid Tom
Open Hi Hat	
	Low Tom
Pedal Hi Hat	
	Hi Floor Tom
Closed Hi Hat	
	Low Floor Tom
	Electric Snare
Hand Clap	
	Acoustic Snare
Side Stick	
	Bass Drum 1
	Acoustic Bass Drum

INPUTTING DRUMS

Unlike other instruments, individual drum sounds do not produce a range of pitches and therefore each requires only one note of the keyboard to trigger it. Consequently a synth **drum kit** voice will usually contain the sounds of a whole range of percussion instruments, each mapped to a different note. Thus, a low C might trigger a bass drum, the F♯ above this a hi-hat, and middle C a bongo.

Many of the sequences in this book need transposing to a different key after recording, a process that increases or decreases all the note numbers in MIDI. Obviously, it is essential not to include the drum track when doing this or your kick drum part will end up being played on the wrong instrument.

Typically, a drum kit voice will include several different variants of each of the main instruments, to suit different musical needs. There will also be a selection of other useful sounds (bongos, hand claps, tambourine) and maybe some esoteric offerings, such as anvils and gongs, that are best reserved for frightening the neighbours.

GM and Drums

As with the numbering of synth voices, General MIDI specifies how manufacturers must map drum sounds to note numbers. The GM percussion map is shown in the keyboard diagram in the margin. The MIDI note numbers range from 35 (the pitch B0, assigned to **acoustic bass drum**) through to 81 (**open triangle**, on pitch A4). The key for middle C (note number 60, or C3) is shaded on the chart. Most synths include further sounds at either end of this scale. GM also perpetuates a long tradition by specifying that channel 10 be reserved for drum kits.

Most synths will enable you to reassign each sound to the most convenient note on the keyboard and to edit or rename each sound. If your synth is not GM, you may wish to re-map its drum kit to match the diagram so that it conforms to this increasingly common specification – it will speed up the process of voicing sequences you buy on disk or borrow from friends and will help to ensure that your own sequences play back more reliably on unfamilar GM equipment.

TIP Many sequencers provide a drum mapping screen which enables note numbers to be reallocated purely inside the sequencer, thus saving the need to alter your synth or drum machine settings. Once you have set up your favourite drum map it can be saved to disk for use in other pieces. This is not only convenient but also avoids the risk of accidentally erasing sounds when trying to move them around inside the synth.

It is often helpful to record at least an outline of the drum part before any of the other tracks in a sequence. This can then replace the disembodied beep of the metronome and will give the right rhythmic feel when recording the rest of the music.

Drum patterns are usually very short and repetitive, so many people find it easiest to step-write them and copy where needed. Step-writing automatically quantizes the notes so remember that bass parts coinciding with the kick drum may easily end up masking it if also quantized too tightly. In general, quantize as few tracks as possible.

TIP If your sequence seems to lack energy, try advancing the drum track very slightly in relation to the others.

Many systems allow step-writing with a mouse. This needs extra care because it will produce uniform velocity levels whereas live drummers, like all musicians, constantly adjust their playing to suit the demands of the piece. You will need to accent important beats when editing and adjust overall levels in the final mix. Here, ghost copies are particularly useful as they automatically pick up any velocity or other changes made to the original pattern. Finally, it is important not to over-boost kick drum parts to compensate for the deficiencies of your monitor speakers – remember that it is almost impossible for domestic equipment to reproduce the bass power of a P.A. system at a live gig.

The Beatles

Most American pop music in the '50s was fronted by a solo vocalist and accompanied by a rhythm section, backing singers, stage band or even full orchestra. The idea of a self-contained group of just four people able to play and sing their own music around the clubs was one of the great contributions the British made to '60s rock music, particularly in Liverpool, and most of all by The Beatles. Their meteoric rise to fame started with Love Me Do *in 1962 although they had, in fact, spent several years before that honing their skills in Hamburg clubs with covers of the likes of Chuck Berry and Little Richard. Buddy Holly was another important influence, as a guitarist who wrote his own songs (unlike Presley, who did not). The Beatles own early material was often irrepressibly optimistic and confidently presented with a nasal Liverpudlian twang a thousand miles distant from the mid-Atlantic drawl of their contemporaries. In fact, they sounded like what they were – ordinary lads from the North who made good by flair and team work. To the teenagers of early '60s Britain, used to unconvincing imitations of American rockers and still inhibited by a rigid class system, this was a revolutionary message. The resulting explosion sent shock waves world wide and resulted briefly in Liverpool becoming the most famous place on earth.*

Please Please Me

This song was The Beatles first Number 1 single, in 1963, and is full of the energy and exuberance which characterises their early work. It also shows how cleverly Lennon and McCartney were able to absorb elements of American Rock & Roll without sacrificing their individuality. There is blues-influenced harmony in the simple alternation of chords I and IV (F and B♭) and in the flattened chords of bar 9, yet the chromatic vocal writing in the chorus and bridge owes much to the European song-writing tradition. Nowhere in American music would you find a lyric like "You don't need me to show the way, love", which is pure Lancashire, while McCartney's unusual ability to sing very high in falsetto is exploited in the top notes of the bvox part. The original song was in E major (a comfortable key for guitarists) but is printed here in F because it involves the use of fewer black notes on the keyboard. Transpose all tracks (except drums) down a semitone when you have finished recording.

RECORDING THE SEQUENCE

As suggested throughout this book, record the drums first to act as a template for the other tracks. Use a **hi tom** in the fills, e.g. bar 9, and notice the appearance of **crash cymbal** to accentuate the chords in the last three bars.

Lead, rhythm and bass guitars, plus drums, is a typical '60s Rock & Roll band format. The lead plays single notes for most of the song, introducing and underlining the melody as well as filling in gaps between the lyrics. The rhythm guitar part looks more complicated because it consists entirely of chords. The layout of these is simple enough for the guitarist, who just strums across the six strings, but a keyboard player will need to use both hands or record the chords in layers in **cycle** mode. For an authentic sound, the note starts should be slightly spread in alternate up and down patterns (see left). This is not as laborious as it looks since you can use a single pair of chords for the whole song, copying out and adjusting pitches where necessary. Staggering note starts can also help disguise insufficient polyphony on the synth.

The **harmonica** (GM 23) simply doubles lead guitar in the intro and in each chorus. If copying across, remember that it should sound an octave higher than the guitar. The bvox part is less reticent than in previous songs in this book – the band were all up-front singers (even Ringo, on occasion). Voicing for this and for the lead vocal will be largely a matter of taste if you are not intending to sing, but bright **trumpet** works well. In the verses the original has bvox singing the same lyrics as the lead but on a single pitch. However, one sustained note will be more effective in an instrumental version.

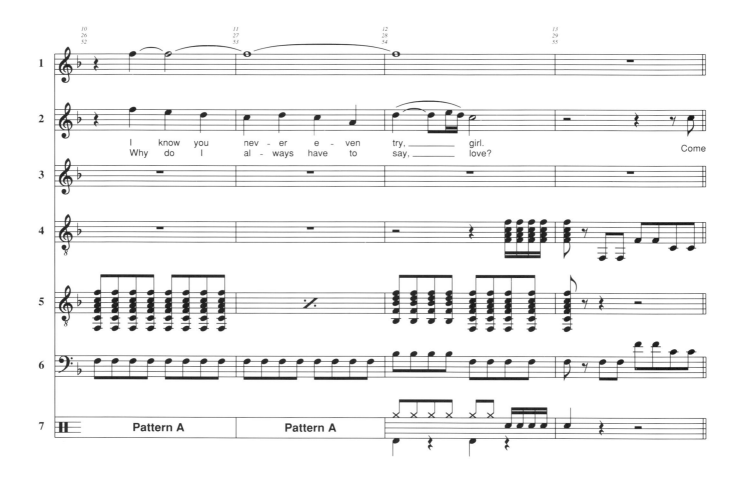

Chorus

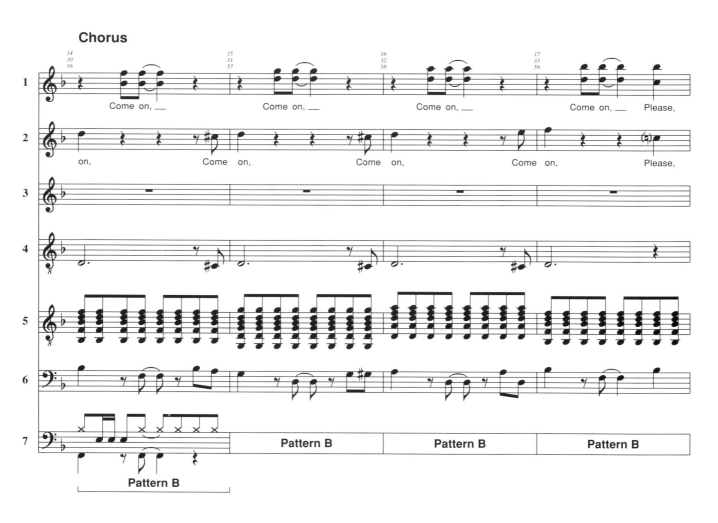

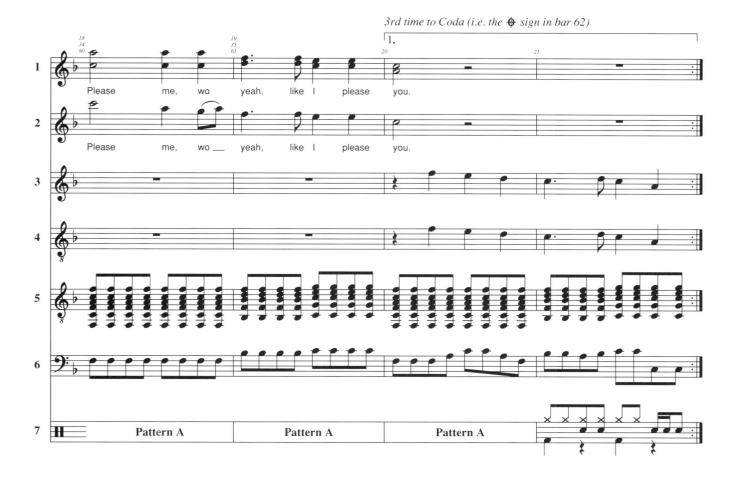

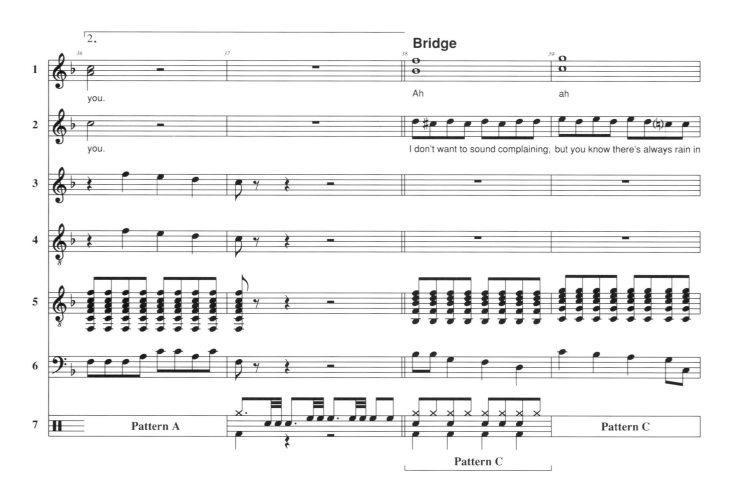

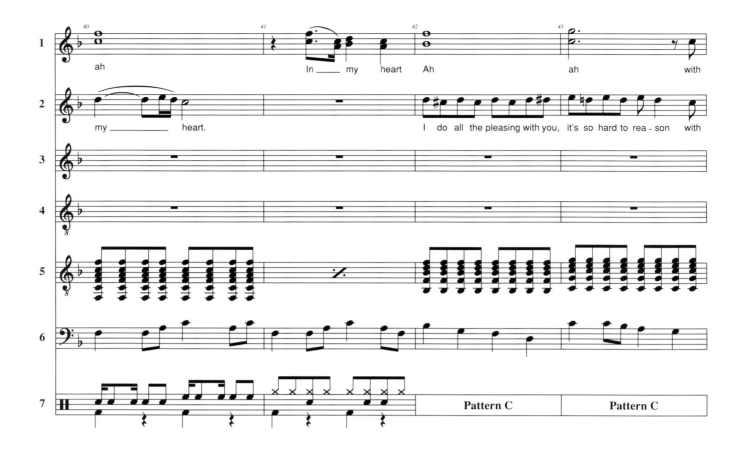

Dal Segno
(i.e. repeat from the
𝄋 sign in bar 6)

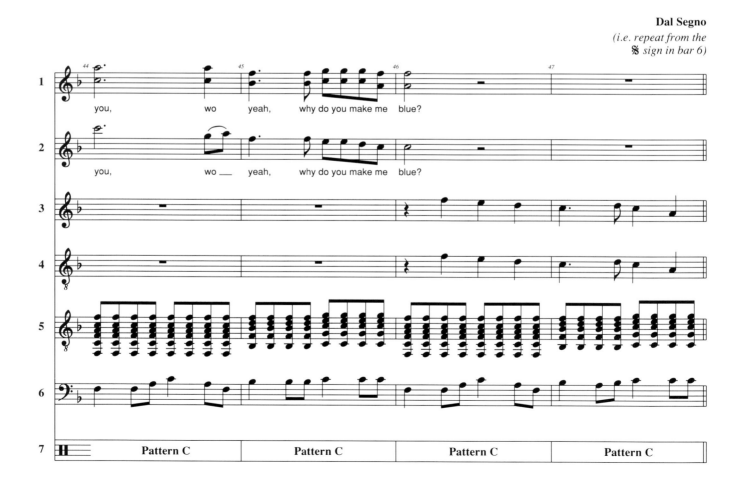

Coda

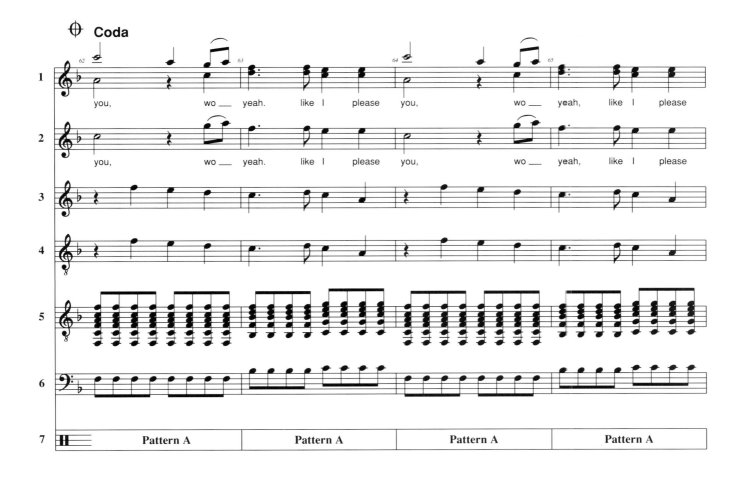

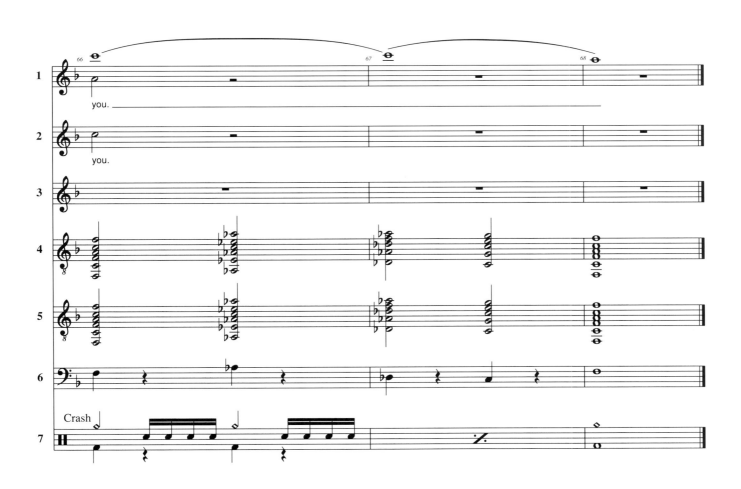

Coming of Age: the late 1960s

By the mid '60s, British Rock & Roll was beginning to take itself very seriously and even the Establishment started to sit up and take notice. The Beatles were awarded MBE honours in 1965 and The Times newspaper acclaimed Lennon and McCartney as the greatest songwriters since Schubert. This caused outrage among its crustier readership who were already appalled to learn that Yesterday *was accompanied by a string quartet, a worrying trespass into the sacrosanct territory of classical music. However, the clearest indicators of rock's ambition to be all-embracing came in 1967. While the Beatles were enjoying unprecedented triumph with their ground-breaking concept album,* Sgt. Pepper, *the surprise hit single of the summer was a song by Procol Harum which cheerfully married the style of Bach to surreal lyrics about getting drunk. It was a massive success.*

A Whiter Shade of Pale

Bar 4   *Play as:*

Bar 6   *Play as:*

Elements of this piece are clearly derived from Bach's *Air on a G-String* which became widely known post-1964 through its use in a cigar commercial. Much of the song's appeal is due to the stately progress of its repeating bass line contrasting with the baroque ornateness of the organ melody. The *acciaccaturas* in bars 3 and 5 will be familiar from *At The Hop* but the ornaments in bars 4 and 6 are shown left. *A Whiter Shade of Pale* also exploited developments in electric organ technology – huge pitch swoops into the Chorus, which shimmers with the characteristic vibrato of the Hammond (or drawbar) organ. Ways of achieving this on synth are mentioned later.

DRUMS AND GUITARS The drum patterns here are not dissimilar to those in the last sequence although the fills are in triplet 16ths, perhaps because of the slower tempo. The chief difference lies in the use of **open hi-hat** (later **splash**) cymbal which, coupled with a wash of reverb, gives the song a much less urgent feel. The rests in the bass part also contribute to steadying the mood. Rhythm guitar chords should be spread, perhaps over slightly more space than last time – with only one of each chord, the direction of strum should be the same each time (*i.e.* bottom to top).

ORGAN Most synths will have a **drawbar organ** sound (GM 17), but to reproduce the effect of its twin keyboards ("manuals") you will need to record the two staves on separate channels. This will prevent note-off problems in places where the melody overlaps with its underlying chords (see bar 2) and will also allow you to balance the two tracks independently. On the record, the lower part is much quieter for most of the song.

The first half of the Chorus needs a rich vibrato. This effect is often implemented by Aftertouch (key pressure); otherwise try using modulation wheel or joystick in these bars. The swoops of pitch which precede this section descend a full octave and return immediately. Originally they would have been made by drawing an electric 'pencil' along a magnetic strip next to the keyboard. MIDI pitchbend can imitate the effect, but check that the synth voice is programmed with a 12 semitone range of pitch bend – many will be preset with much less than this and will need editing if you want to reproduce Procol Harum's radical flourishes here.

VOCAL Notation makes a poor job of illustrating the precise rhythm of the solo vocal, which by this time was taking on something of the freedom of blues and gospel singing. Listening to the original recording will give you a fix on the style and provide the lyrics for the second verse if you want to sing along – otherwise record on **alto sax**.

LAYOUT Bar 1–32 are repeated, after which the Intro starts for a third time (bars 65–69), then jumping to the Coda printed at bar 70. The song fades out during a final, more elaborate repetition of the Chorus which you can reconstruct from the model in bar 73.

Words and music by
Keith Reid and Gary Brooker

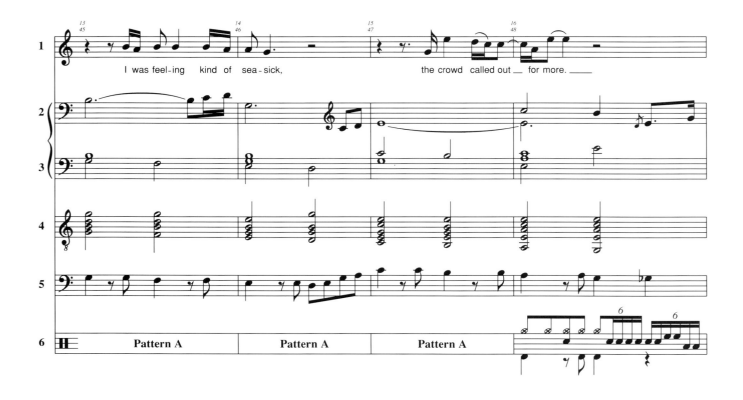

I was feel-ing   kind of sea-sick,   the crowd called out __ for more. ___

Pattern A   Pattern A   Pattern A

The room was hum-ming hard – er   as the ceil-ing   flew a – way ___

Splash

Pattern B

Fill (as bar 16)

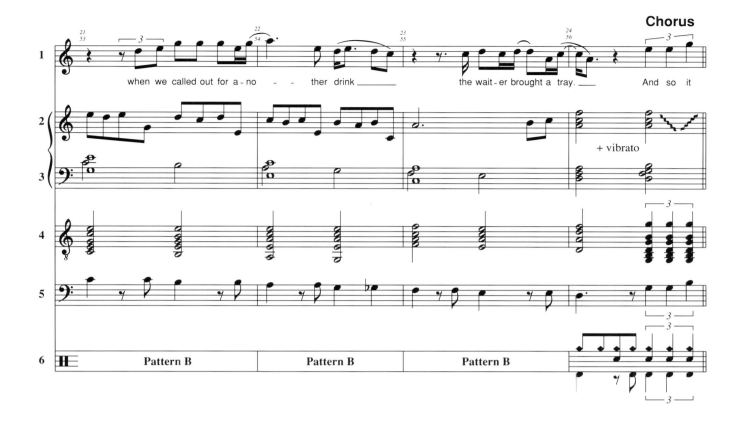

when we called out for a-no - - ther drink _____ the wait-er brought a tray. _____ And so it

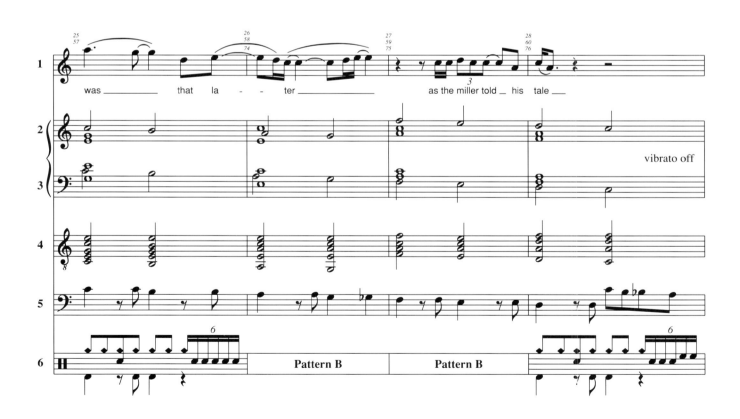

was _____ that la - - ter _____ as the miller told _ his tale _____

Last time: fade-out on all tracks

that her face at first just ghost-ly   turned a whiter _ shade of pale. ___

Alternative guitar part for 2nd chorus:

Pattern B   Pattern B   Pattern B

✛ **Coda**

Repeat Chorus (from bar 74) to fade

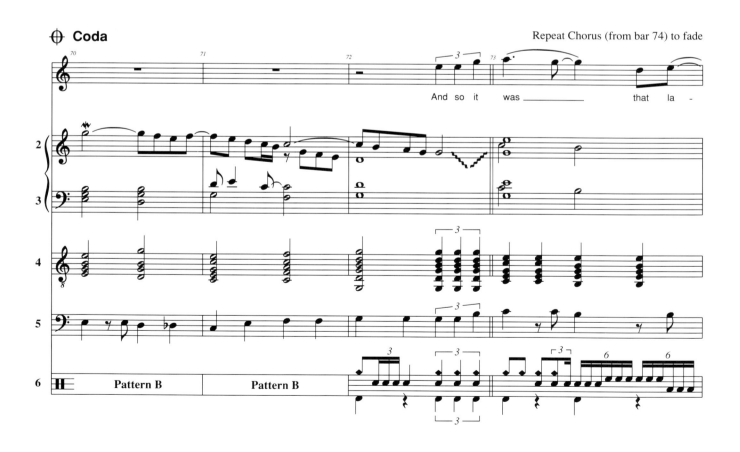

And so it was _____ that la -

Pattern B   Pattern B

Effects

*The term **effects** covers a number of ways of processing an audio signal to enhance the raw sound. Almost the only studio effect available in the early years of Rock & Roll was an electro-mechanical reverb. This was produced by channelling the signal through a resonant room, or through a large steel plate or spring. The development of the transistor and, in the late '60s, the integrated circuit, enabled technicians to build not only electronic reverb systems, but a number of other signal-processing devices that rock musicians quickly adopted in their search for a wider range of sounds. Modern synths generally include a selection of such effects which can be applied to individual voices. Stand alone multi-effects units are also available for connection between your synth and monitor speakers, and may be triggered by MIDI Controller messages from the sequencer.*

REVERB
Most pop records use a small amount of reverb to enhance the sound – around 0.5 seconds is standard, although longer reverb on vocals is common. Drum patterns are easily muddied by reverb, except for the snare which can take as much as 1.5 seconds if a big rock sound is needed (see also Gate below). **Reverse reverb**, in which the after-sound builds to an abrupt cut-off, is a special effect sometimes used on cymbals. **Early reflections** are the parts of the after-sound that are heard before the main wash of reverb. Separate control of these will make a digital reverb more realistic.

DELAY
Unlike reverb, delay gives a distinct echo effect. Timing is often set to match the tempo of the song so that you get, say, two or four echoes per bar. Sometimes used on the final words of vocal phrases and on snare drum tracks. **Stereo delay**, with different delay times for left and right channels, is a special effect that causes a sound to bounce between the monitor speakers.

CHORUS
A randomly changing, very short delay with some shift of pitch. By thickening the sound it can give the impression of several musicians performing the same part. Useful for making a solo string instrument sound like a complete section of players.

PHASER
A short delay designed to introduce phase differences which give a characteristic swirling and swishing sound, particularly used on guitar and electric piano.

FLANGER
A more pronounced form of phasing, using a longer delay time. Most effective on electric guitar, it is sometimes used on the reverb rather than on the direct signal.

OVERDRIVE
Deliberate distortion, particularly favoured by Heavy Metal guitarists and sometimes used in conjunction with a flanger.

ROTARY SPEAKERS
Simulates the rotating 'Leslie' speakers of the Hammond Organ, producing a rich chorus effect with slowly changing pitch shifts (imitating the Doppler effect).

EQUALIZER
Enables different parts of the frequency range to be cut or boosted. An increase in low frequency gives a sound more depth, while boosting high frequency adds brightness. More sophisticated EQ is found on studio mixing desks.

COMPRESSOR
Compression evens up the dynamic range of a signal, reducing the loudest parts and bringing up the softer levels. Often employed for recording vocals in the studio, it is also useful for containing the response of "lively" synth voices such as sax. Widely over-used in pop music mixes, where it suppresses the natural variety of human input.

EXCITER
Adds extra high partials and a small amount of compression to enhance clarity. Useful for giving bite to bland sounds or adding focus to a dull kick drum.

GATE
An electronic switch that mutes the signal when it drops below a pre-set level, typically leaving just the attack of the note without any decay. Often used to give drums (especially the snare) extra punch and to remove any noise from silences. **Gated reverb** gives a distinctive burst of reverberation lacking any natural decay.

Sequence 7

Doing A Simple Thing Well

The ability to absorb and reinterpret musical styles has always been a feature of rock music. The classical influences in A Whiter Shade of Pale *were the precursors of a trend which ultimately produced showpieces like Queen's* Bohemian Rhapsody *and even The Who's "rock opera",* Tommy. *Later chapters deal with the even more important influences of Latin-American and Carribean music. However, rock is also adept at recycling its own tried-and-trusted formulæ: few groups have been more successful at this than The Hollies. The perennially popular ballad,* He Ain't Heavy, *owes as much to older MOR traditions as it does to more contemporary developments. With its traditional harmonies and lush string orchestration, it probably sounded comfortingly old-fashioned in 1969. From the perspective of another quarter-century of innovation and re-cycling, it now just seems timeless.*

He Ain't Heavy

The music of *He Ain't Heavy* is by the American jazz pianist and singer Bobby Scott, whose compositional pedigree included studies with a pupil of Debussy. The Hollies also wrote their own songs (as a team effort credited under the pseudonym L. Ransford) but the catchy, harmony-laden pop style of all their records is characterised by strong vocal arrangements. The vocal and bvox parts in this song need to be well to the front, using voices such as **sax** and perhaps **oboe** for clarity.

STRINGS

The string part is silent in Verse 1 but plays an increasingly important role as the song progresses. The *coll' 8va* instruction in bar 36 indicates that the first violins duplicate the melody line (only) an octave higher until the *loco* ('in place') marking in bar 41. This section may need to be recorded separately so that the tranposition does not change the underlying chords as well. As with *Puppy Love* in Sequence 4, the use of a **string ensemble** voice (GM 49/50) should give the effect of a large section of players. In Verse 4, the triple beams over chords indicate that each note should be rapidly repeated. This is known as tremolo and is a classic device for increasing a sound's intensity. GM offers **tremolo strings** as a separate voice (45). If your synth does not implement this, try repeating each chord eight times per beat.

PIANO

The piano is kept well back in the original, and should never dominate the mix. We have outlined a simple rock pattern based on the chord symbols which are printed above the stave: experienced players may want to use the symbols to produce a more elaborate part. In either case, there is no piano in bars 36–48.

HARMONICA

Much of the distinctive appeal of *He Ain't Heavy* comes from the plaintive harmonica solo which opens the song. Accurate pitch and rhythm make any music recognisable but it is the subtle changes in pitch and tone colour, impossible to show in notation, which ensure that it is also memorable, especially in solos. It is therefore worth lavishing some care on these details to reproduce the expressive, slightly over-blown character of this part. Here are some ideas on how you can use MIDI to achieve this.

Pitch Bend

➡ The grid shows how several notes start with a small slide up (from about half a semitone below the written pitches) and how the *crescendo* tempts the player into blowing slightly sharp (positive pitch bend) through the long note. Notice that space is needed to set the control before the first note and that others need to be slightly clipped for the same reason.

Volume

➡ The *crescendo* through a single note requires the use of MIDI controller 7 (volume) or 11 (expression) – these controllers will also help with the *diminuendo* in bar 3.

Modulation

➡ The term modulation usually refers to the small fluctuations in pitch which live players call *vibrato* and use to add colour and intensity to the sound.

Our book, Music in Sequence, gives some detailed help on using MIDI Controller data on pages 86-87.

The synth user can reproduce these essential aspects of live peformance either by writing the data needed on the sequencer, using the grids below for reference, or by using the synth's **pitch bend** control, **volume** pedal and **modulation** wheel (or **aftertouch** facility). Synth controls can be used while recording or by overdubbing their movements onto the track after basic notes are recorded. Notice that, to avoid affecting later data on the track, Volume should be reset to normal after use while pitch bend must return to zero.

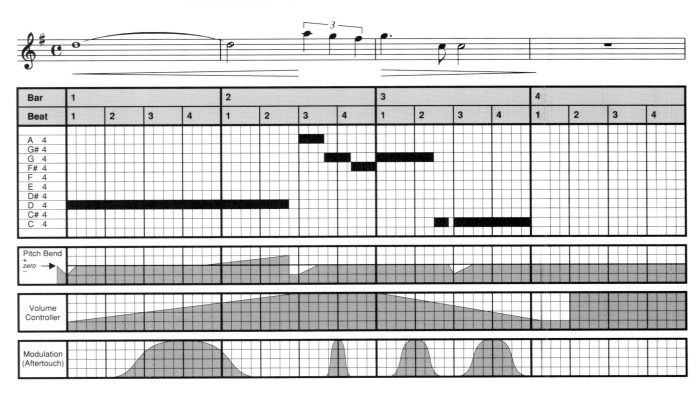

He Ain't Heavy ... He's My Brother   1969

Sequence 8
Under Cover

Beneath the skin of every song is a skeleton which shapes its features. The combination of chord patterns, melody and structure, together with its lyrics, makes a song unique. Get it right and you have something special which exists independently of the people who perform it and can survive, even benefit from, countless different interpretations. By common consent, the most-covered song is McCartney's Yesterday, *which has been recorded over 2000 times in versions ranging from supermarket muzak to Motown. The song in this chapter started life in Britain as a heavily blues-influenced stomper by Fleetwood Mac. However, a few subtle changes to the structure, a new bass part, the replacement of kit drums by congas and bongos and a smoothly lyrical guitar solo make the cover of* Black Magic Woman *by the American group Santana, into a more seductive creature altogether.*

MODES

One of the most significant influences on Rock & Roll in the late '60s was the adoption of the modal scales which formed the basis of traditional folk music and had already been taken up by jazz players. Previously, most popular western music had been major, blue notes notwithstanding, or just occasionally minor. In fact, the major and minor scales are just two of many possible ways of subdividing an octave into tones and semitones. Such patterns of notes are known as **modes**.

Try playing a scale of white notes only, from D to D an octave higher. These notes form the pattern of the Dorian mode and are used as the basis of *Black Magic Woman*. Although the pitches are the same as those in C major, the whole song focuses on the note D rather than C (take a look at the bass part and vocal). The almost total absence of notes outside the mode, together with the infrequent changes of chord, give an hypnotically static feel to the harmony.

Of course, modal music does not have to use entirely white notes. Like the major scale (the Ionian mode), all modes can be transposed to any pitch – it is their particular patterns of tones and semitones which gives them their character. Two other modes commonly found in rock music are the Aeolian (try the white note scale from A to A) and Mixolydian (G to G). The first is used in the melody of *Stairway To Heaven* (Sequence 9) and in Paul Simon's *Sound of Silence*, while *A Hard Day's Night* by the Beatles has the major third and minor seventh characteristic of the Mixolydian.

Black Magic Woman

The first four bars of Fleetwood Mac's original are given below, and should be compared with bars 43–46 of Santana's cover version, printed later in this chapter:

It kicks off immediately with the vocal, drums and bass outlining a heavily syncopated tango rhythm underneath. Santana's cover makes several crucial changes to the form of the song, adding a riff-based introduction and a guitar solo to the start and a wild, voodoo-like Coda at the end. Both versions have an instrumental in its traditional position mid-way through the song. Although we have space to print only an abridged version, the whole introductory sequence is given, along with a transcription of the sweetly lyrical guitar solo by Carlos Santana which sets the mood for the rest of the piece. This is reinforced by the use of Latin American percussion.

DRUMS

Congas are tall, floor-standing drums, usually played in pairs with one tuned lower than the other. **Bongos** also come in pairs but are much smaller. Both are hit with the hands. **Timbales** are like bongos, but played using sticks. These, and various cymbals, are used throughout the sequence along with an occasional note on kick drum at changes of section. The drum track can be tightly quantized; notice the accents on the cymbal part, but take care not to let them overwhelm the softer Latin drums.

BASS

The notes here are straightforward but much of the laid-back feel of the record is created by the bass playing well behind the beat. Record the part as written and then experiment with quite a substantial amount of MIDI **delay** on the track.

In the Intro, a full seven semitones of pitch bend is needed for the slide from A down to D. Such a large amount of bend will probably have to be programmed into the synth, since the default setting is usually no more than a tone. Remember to release the A slightly early to allow the wheel to return to normal before you play the D.

TIP It may be easier to record bars 6–7 without pitch bend and then write the controller data into the sequence afterwards. This avoids the need for a gap in the sound, allowing precise control over the position of the pitch bend off instruction. The finished pattern can then be copied as needed.

ORGAN

Two keyboard sounds are needed for this song: a soft, flutey **electric organ** at the start and a **piano** or **electric piano** in the Release (starting at bar 36) and Verses. Notice that only the Intro uses both treble and bass staves.

GUITAR

The shape of the guitar, and the hand positions it uses, can often result in musical lines and chord layouts which do not suit the keyboard player too well. However, it is possible for the synth user to create an amazingly realistic guitar solo, particularly with the aid of some pitch bend (a 2 semitone range is needed for this part).

To help you do this, we have devised a special notation using grey notes (which can be read as normal while you familiarize yourself with the melody). Ultimately, these notes should not actually be pressed on the keyboard, but each should be produced by using pitch bend while the previous note is sustained. The slur over the top of such notes shows how long this should go on for. So, in bars 7 and 8 (see right) strike the D and *hold the key down* while *moving the pitch bend up* to create the E in the next bar. Let the wheel fall back to return to D  for the next note. Try to move the wheel to match the rhythms shown.

In bars 24 and 28 you need to restrike the C (printed D) on the third beat, with pitch bend still up. This will all take a little practice – listening to Santana's original recording will undoubtedly help – but you may well be delighted with the final result.

The wiggly lines in the Intro show where the guitarist coloured the tone with feedback: aftertouch modulation will give life to these and other long notes. The hanging slurs in bar 21 indicate that each note should be allowed to sustain through the bar. Notice that the guitar solo in bars 22–33 is an octave higher than printed, although due to the guitar's "transposing clef", this means that what you see is actually what you hear, for once! The six downward diagonals in bar 34 indicate where Santana let the entire last chord of the solo sink as the sound faded. The guitar should step out of the limelight after its solo, although shorter chords can be staccato to add rhythmic drive.

Black Magic Woman

Words and original music by Peter A. Green
Arranged by Santana

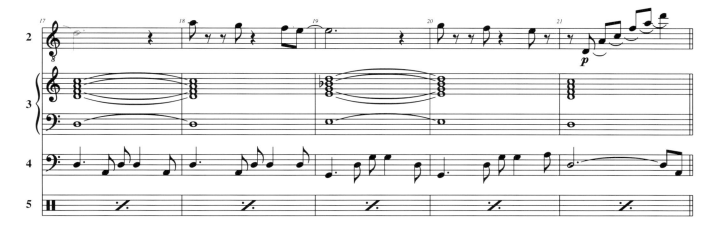

Instrumental

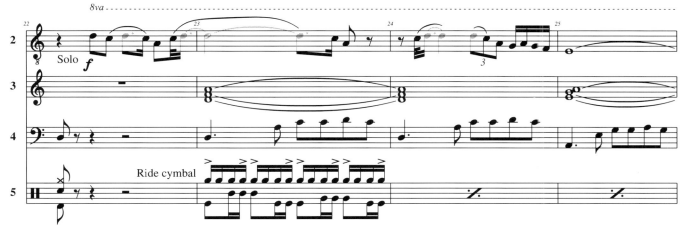

Release

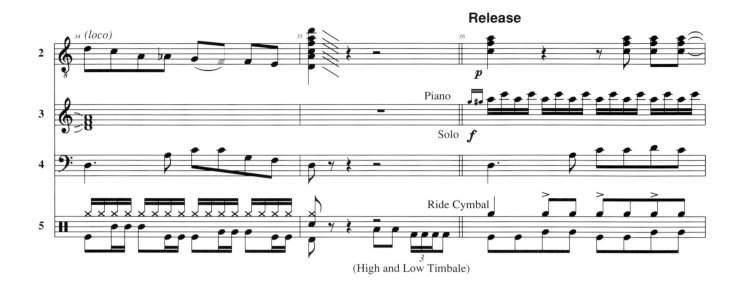

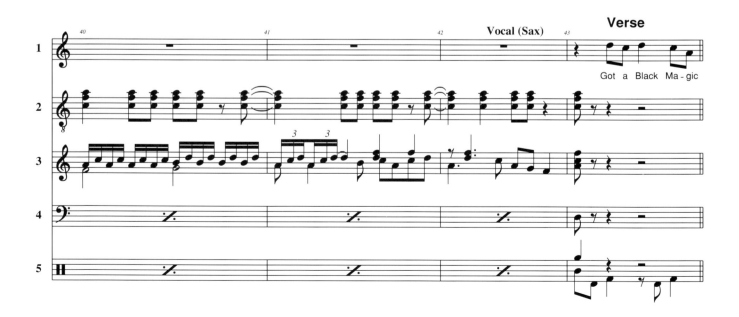

Sequence 9

Rock Anthems: the 1970s

Everyone has their list of all-time great rock tracks and few would fail to include Led Zeppelin's Stairway to Heaven, *although its gentle, folk-influenced opening is a surprise given the band's heavy reputation. By now the rock scene had moved far beyond the largely Anglo-American influences of the early sixties. The Beatles had embraced Indian music; Ska and Reggae appeared from Jamaica and Afro-American music reasserted itself with Motown and Soul. Groups such as Jefferson Airplane and Deep Purple began to exploit the technology of rock – heavy distortion and electronic effects – while Jimi Hendrix and others developed the electric guitar into an instrument of pyrotechnic virtuosity or a weapon of mass destruction, depending on your viewpoint. Ultimately, this ambitious diversity gave way to the calculated anarchy of Punk Rock with its sneering disregard for any traditional concepts of melody, harmony or structure. In the longer term, however, songs like* Stairway *probably owe their perennial popularity as much to their use of age-old techniques as to any heavy-metal credentials.*

The delicate introduction to this song is almost a rite of passage for guitarists and can be heard in virtually any instrument store on a Saturday morning. To match the resonant acoustic guitar, keyboard players should try using the sustain pedal on this part, changing it with each new bass note. Pitch bend of a semitone will be needed for the occasional bent note (indicated, as in the previous chapter, by grey notation).

Around the guitar part, sustaining its chords, is the centuries-old sound of a **recorder** consort. These simple wooden pipes are difficult to play in tune, especially the lowest one (which tends to blow sharp). Record the two tracks on different channels and slightly detune one with an initial pitch bend setting to reproduce the wavery, almost sour effect to be heard on the record. Recorders are also very responsive to dynamic change and each four-bar phrase will benefit from a crescendo towards the third bar each time. However, don't quantise velocity or rhythms too fiercely on these tracks.

The vocal reinforces the ancient resonances of the song with a sinuous melody which uses just six different pitches of the Aeolian mode. The plaintive slides in Robert Plant's expressive singing can again be suggested with pitchbend (perhaps on **sax**): you will need to set a full tone of bend for this track. The first 36 bars of the song, printed here, are probably the most easy to sequence but a full score of the complete song is available in music shops for those who want to explore further.

Stairway to Heaven   1972

*Words and music by
Jimmy Page and Robert Plant*

There's a

In bars 21–36 the guitar repeats bars 5–20.

Life After Folk: Paul Simon

Longevity is rather a rare commodity in rock careers – sex and drugs take their toll but the main problem is adaptability. The public quickly tires of hearing the same old tricks, and only those artists who can constantly re-invent themselves and develop their musical ideas are likely to keep the hits flowing. Paul Simon's extraordinary versatility and obsessive attention to detail produced a career which took off back in the early '60s as the songwriting half of Simon and Garfunkel. Then followed a string of solo albums which encompassed material ranging from folk- and blues-inspired ballads to explorations of indigenous African and South American music. The song in this chapter comes from his 1975 album Still Crazy After All These Years. *Simon's perfectionism extends into all areas of the song's production, and the care taken over recording and mixing its delicate but complex web of backing material offers an intriguing challenge to the sequencer user.*

I Do It For Your Love

The structure of this song, with its three verses, bridge and instrumental, maintains links with music from much earlier. After his split from Art Garfunkel, Paul Simon took song-writing classes (although it is hard to imagine what he thought needed improvement after the colossal success of hits like *The Sound Of Silence* and *Bridge Over Troubled Water*). What is evident, however, is the increased sophistication of his harmony – more jazz-influenced than most contemporaries – which allows apparent clashes like the A♭/A♮ in bar 26 to sound both natural and expressive.

We have made as accurate a transcription as practicable of this song so that its distinctive palette of colours and textures can be reproduced. Simon's singing style is softly lyrical (try **pan flute** on the vocal) so it is vital that backing tracks such as the guitar and piano parts in the Bridge section are kept well back in the mix. The **electric piano** sound should be rounded and gentle and not too bottom heavy (synths sometimes use pipe organ terminology to describe lower-sounding timbres as 16′ rather than 8′).

For reasons of space, stave 5 of the score is used for most of the miscellaneous instrumental music, although it will probably be simplest to designate separate tracks for **guitar 2**, **oboe**, **strings**, etc. on the sequencer. In the final bar, the pause sign (⌒) indicates a chord that should last longer than normal. This can be done either by extending into a new bar or with a sudden change to a much slower tempo. A global *diminuendo* would sound good here, fading the music to nothing.

Most of the techniques needed in this sequence have already been introduced in earlier chapters – for instance, using MIDI Controllers 7 or 11 to make the oboe *crescendo* crops up in Sequence 7. You may need to extend your drum map to accommodate some of the extra instruments shown in the grids overleaf (a very high and extremely quiet **glockenspiel** note can be used if your synth does not include **triangle**). The original recording also contains a few very soft electric tom notes which we have omitted in the interests of simplicity: if total accuracy is your main concern, these can be taken down from the record. In any case, remember that the entire percussion part is very discreet throughout.

Paul Simon's studio craft produces a particularly clear and transparent stereo mix which is the result of careful instrument placing and balance. Experiment with different pan settings until all tracks are audible even at low volume before saving the settings into the sequence. He also makes subtle use of guitar effects – flanger adds a noticeable gloss to the Intro, for example. If your synth incorporates these, here would be a good opportunity to discover what they can offer.

DRUM PATTERNS

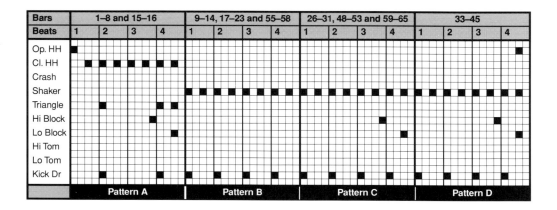

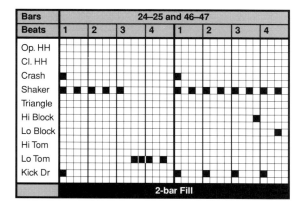

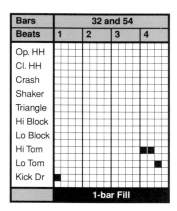

I Do It For Your Love

1975

Words and music by
Paul Simon

80 bpm

Verses 1 and 2

1. We were married on a rain - y day; _____ the sky was yellow anc the grass was gray. _____
2. The rooms were musty and the pipes _ were old; _____ all that winter we shared _ a cold. _____

Verse 2 only

We signed the papers and we drove a - way.
Drank all the orange juice that we could hold.

1.

I do it for _ your love. _

Verse 3

Sequence 11

Euro–Disco

The Eurovision Song Contests, with their virtual guarantee of bland jauntiness or mawkish sentiment, became the butt of jokes almost as soon as they began in 1956. Few people who were alive and still conscious in the '70s will forget the sound of Katie Boyle solemnly reading the results to a multi-lingual audience. "Norway: nul points!" Few entrants survived the ridicule that was heaped upon many winning songs, although Abba's victory in 1974 with Waterloo *led to a remarkable run of chart successes and briefly made the group into Sweden's second biggest export after Volvo cars. As you might expect, the musical ingredients were simple and easily digestible but production was slick and the records provided easy listening and good-time dance music for those who found other developments altogether too dangerous. The recent revival of interest in '70s dance music just goes to show that you can never underestimate your audience.*

Money, Money, Money

Popular songs in a minor key are relatively uncommon. This one also shows the influence of early sequencer technology in the repeating 4-note synth riffs and use of drum machine patterns – much of Abba's stage material was pre-recorded. Notice also the **timpani** (GM 48) notes which act as fills and sign the song off. These should have plenty of reverb.

Another unusual feature is the *ritenuto,* a gradual slowing up in bars 19–20. This change will need to be made on the sequencer's Tempo or Master Track, taking the speed down in stages to about 60 bpm by the end of bar 20 before resetting 120 bpm at the *a tempo* in bar 22. Note that this "rit." does not happen in Verse 2. Bar 21 has only two beats and requires a $\frac{2}{4}$ time signature.

TIP If your sequencer does not allow a change of time signature in mid-song, experiment with using longer note values at a faster tempo to achieve the same effect.

Many people will be already familiar with Abba's recorded sound and therefore able to find the closest match their synth offers. If you have not heard the record, remember that bass and drums need extra weight in disco music and all tracks can be tightly quantized. The piano sound in this song is very bright and the lower vocal in the chorus could be assigned to a different channel and possibly transposed up an octave – but it must not obscure the lead. Like much disco music, *Money* is repetitive and the full song can be assembled as follows:

➤ Record all tracks up to bar 40, including the internal repeats at bars 7-10 and 24-27.

➤ Copy bars 5-20 into 41-56, and bars 22-38 into 57-73 to make Verse 2 (this avoids copying bar 21, which is not repeated).

➤ Record the 2nd time bar (74) followed by a further repeat of the Chorus (24- 40) this time transposed up a semitone (remember not to transpose the drums).

Finally, add the drum flourish printed below:

1   I work all night, I work all day
To pay the bills I have to pay – ain't it sad –
And still there never seems to be
A single penny left for me – that's too bad.
    In my dreams I have a plan,
    If I got me a wealthy man
    I wouldn't have to work at all,
    I'd fool around and have a ball: *Chorus*

2   A man like that is hard to find,
But I can't get him off my mind – ain't it sad –
And if he happens to be free
I bet he wouldn't fancy me – that's too bad.
    So I must leave, I'll have to go
    To Las Vegas or Monaco
    And win a fortune in a game,
    My life would never be the same: *Chorus*

Words and music by
Benny Andersson and Björn Ulvaeus

Sequence 12

Caribbean Influences

Abba's rival as the most commercially successful group of the '70s was the German-based Boney M. Although promoted initially for their 'Eurodisco' sound of pounding drums and sequenced riffs, the group's four Caribbean-born singers were soon encouraged to explore much wider sources of material, including a cover of Harry Belafonte's 1957 hit, Mary's Boy Child, *the old Jamaican nursery rhyme* Brown Girl In The Ring *and, on the flip side, the classic West Indian song featured below,* Rivers Of Babylon. *This, too, was a cover – of a version recorded in 1970 by the Jamaican Reggae trio, The Melodians.*

A vibrant tradition of popular music had developed in the West Indies during the '60s and '70s, drawing on such varied influences as Rhythm and Blues, the close vocal harmony of Doo Wop and the Trinidadian calypso. Strong back beats within a relatively slow tempo gave rise to the descriptions 'Rock Steady' and, later, 'Reggae' as bass parts became heavier. A strong Rastafarian influence was responsible for the Old Testament references in many of the songs. The outside world initially received only the occasional hint of these new developments and even in Jamaica local hits were banned from the radio. It is significant that one of Reggae's greatest songs, Bob Marley's I Shot The Sheriff, *first became internationally known through a European cover version by Eric Clapton. Boney M's version of* Rivers Of Babylon *stands at a rather strange crossroads. Its success introduced many people to a new type of black music, and yet the arrangement, with its sounds of ocean waves and Steel Band carnival music, can be criticised for giving only a tourist's perspective on the culture.*

Rivers of Babylon

The musical structure of the song is extremely simple – two 8-bar sections flanking one which is (surprisingly) of 9 bars. These are strung together in a chain of repeats. The Boney M recording also has a Desert Island Discs style introduction, using a slow version of the vocals and bvox from bars 1–16, backed by the sound of waves and seagulls. We have not printed this, but you could reconstruct it with the help of GM 123 (**seashore**) if you wish.

Bars 20 and 29

Unlike the complex harmony of the last few sequences, the effect of *Rivers of Babylon* depends on the simple alternation of just three chords and the cumulatively hypnotic repetitions. Vocals and bass for the whole song are printed overleaf, along with a fully-scored transcription of the first section. The guitar continues throughout using the same rhythm, so you can simply copy the part out following the chord symbols given with the bass part. See left for the layout of the **F** chord needed by guitar in the middle section. Only a single backbeat drum pattern is required, along with three fills for toms (or timbales) which link the sections:

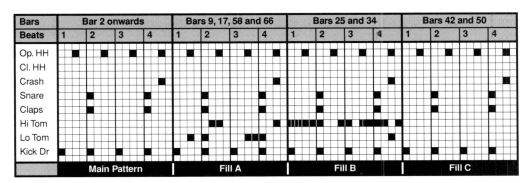

Many synths include a **steel pans** voice (GM115): these were traditionally empty oil drums whose ends were hammered into segments that sound different notes when struck. A resonant and slightly de-tuned marimba, even though actually a wooden

instrument, may be an acceptable substitute. In this song steel pans are used for the repeats of the first two sections (bars 10–16 and 27–33). For the second of these you can create a part using the same rhythms as before over the new chord symbols – the **F** chord needed in bar 29 is shown left. The instruction *D.S. (Dal Segno)* in bar 50 means repeat from the sign in bar 2. This provides the material for a fade out. Notice that this time steel pans have new material, which is printed on stave 4.

Rivers of Babylon   1978

Words and music traditional Jamaican
arr. Dowe, McNaughton, Farian, Reyam

Sequence 13

Hello to the Past: the 1980s

Throughout the 1970s, one of the most significant black influences on American music came from the Detroit-based record label Motown (from "motor town"). Fiercely proud of its independence, the company especially promoted an amalgam of Rhythm & Blues and Gospel music which, since 1969, had become known as Soul. The style was often fervently emotional with singers working up a lather of sobs, swoops and exuberant falsetto. Lionel Ritchie was lead vocalist with The Commodores, one of the most successful Motown groups of the seventies. He has calmed down a lot since then, prompting one sardonic commentator to dub him "the black Barry Manilow". Nonetheless, a decision to go solo in 1981 produced a string of beautifully crafted ballads which maintain echoes of Soul while appealing to a more middle of the road audience.

Hello

As with most memorable songs, the musical material in *Hello* is disarmingly simple. The verse is based on a repeating two-bar piano riff in the Aeolian mode (the white-note scale from A to A – see page 60). The chorus (bars 13–21) uses a plain sequence of chords a fifth apart which cycle round twice. Ritchie short-circuits a complete "cycle of fifths" by neatly jumping from B♭ to E, rather than E♭, in bars 15 and 20, thereby confirming A minor as the key of the song. The use of the flat 2 or "Neapolitan" chord (B♭ in this key) is an age-old device of European music for adding a touch of surprise to a cadence.

MASTERTRACK

Notice that at the end of each chorus (bars 19 and 39) we have inserted a $\frac{2}{4}$ bar which is needed to account for a pause of two beats in the original song. There is also a *rit.* at the very end. See page 75 for further explanation of how to set up these changes on a Master or Tempo Track before you start recording.

PIANO AND BASS

In the last two bars, the direction ℗ℯ𝒹. indicates that the pianist is to use the sustaining pedal to keep all notes sounding to the end of the song. If you do not have one of these, the effect can be written in using Controller 64. Alternatively, all notes can be manually lengthened. The pedal will also add lustre to the sound if used across identical chords in the rest of the song.

At the top of page 85, the bass part needs some pitch bend. The first of these implies a slide up of 5 semitones (don't re-sound the D printed in grey). The second can use the same amount of slide, descending towards the low E, which this time should be played as normal.

VOCAL AND DRUMS

Notation is nowhere near accurate enough to show Ritchie's exact placing of each note in the vocal – listen to his recording before playing the part in freehand. **Sax** will be the obvious choice for this, recorded with as much emotional charge as you can muster. Those who insist on step writing will need to use quarter- and eighth-note triplets (4T and 8T) in some bars. The original has a third verse instrumental on guitar (not printed here) followed by another chorus. If you want to expand the sequence, you could try improvising the guitar solo, based on the chords in the piano part. We have also made some minor simplifications to the drum part, which consists almost entirely of open and closed hi-hat with occasional snare drum notes for emphasis.

OTHER PARTS

Track 3 can be assigned to **electric piano** at the start, changing to **oboe** at bar 21 and **guitar** at 25. There are also various atmospheric effects that can be added to the score. These include a held A minor chord on some sort of glittery FX pad, wreathing the introductions to each verse. You may also like to experiment with the following delicate, 32T arpeggio pattern which decorates bars 7–8 and 29–30. The instruction *15ma* indicates notes which are to be played **two** octaves higher than printed. These will probably be above the range of your keyboard, although the synth will still be able to sound them if you step-write or transpose this section on the sequencer.

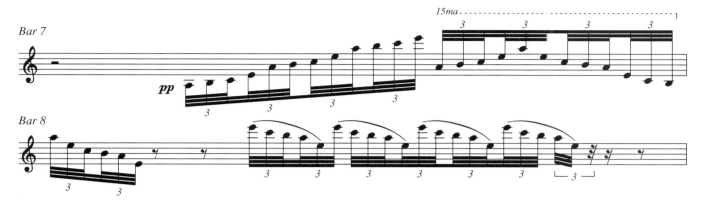

Hello

1983/4

Words and music by Lionel Ritchie

been a-lone with you in-side my ____ mind ____   And   in   my dreams I've kissed your lips   a thou-sand times   I

Sequence 14

Cynicism and the CD

Rock music has always been married to its technology which, by the early '80s, had developed sufficiently to give musicians an unprecedented freedom of expression. For years, though, most domestic consumers had been restricted to the standard vinyl formats of 45 rpm single and LP album which had been around since Rock & Roll began. A generation raised on music of the '50s and '60s had grown up and now had money to spend. For them, the introduction of the digital Compact Disc in 1983 provided an alluring new toy. Alienated by Punk and confused by the androgenous messages of New Romantic bands such as Boy George's Culture Club, this CD generation liked its music accessible – although it didn't mind an ironic slant to maintain a degree of street cred. Dire Straits, with a mixture of blues-based harmony and world-weary lyricism fitted the bill perfectly. Their 1985 album Brothers In Arms *was digitally recorded for the new CD format and became one of the decade's biggest sellers. Only a cynic would suggest that this was due in no small part to the marketing triumph of the Live Aid charity concert or the bizarre revelation that Princess Diana roller-skated around the corridors of Kensington Palace listening to the band on her Walkman.*

Money for Nothing	1985

Money for Nothing was written by two of the decade's most successful song-writers: Dire Straits' guitarist Mark Knopfler (whose *Private Dancer* was a massive hit for Tina Turner) and Sting, lead singer of The Police (which had just disbanded).

The song is effectively in two parts: a slow, synthesized introduction which features Sting's distinctive falsetto vocals (sung at the printed pitch), followed by one of Rock's rauchiest guitar riffs to accompany the ironic growl of Knopfler. The patterns for the Intro are underpinned by 28 bars of sustained chord (in the abbreviated notation below notice that the first chord remains unchanged for 10 bars).

INTRO

Words and music by Mark Knopfler and Sting

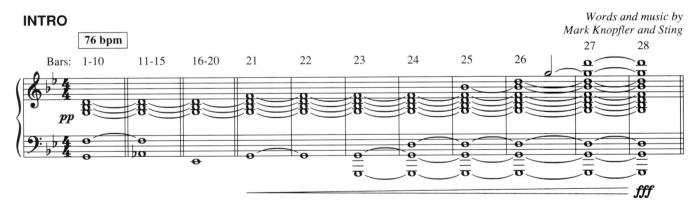

This backing should create an atmospheric texture, similar to that on the original recording. Try a **warm pad** voicing, but also experiment with copying a few notes of the chord for assignment to 'synth FX' voices ('atmosphere', 'echoes', etc.). The chord will need to be built up in layers, adding as many extra notes of a **Gm7** chord in the last eight bars as your synth's polyphony will allow. This will assist the *crescendo*, which needs to be as big as possible.

INTRO RIFF

The following sequencer riff fades in at bar 6 and continues to the end of the Intro (dropping in volume during bars 11–15). We used a dry **marimba** for this texture:

INTRO VOCAL

Sting's singing is highly compressed on the record, so the four patterns could use a smoothly synthetic vocal sound (a preset called something like 'angels' may be your best bet).

SYNTH FILLS

In between the vocal patterns are some quiet fills using yet another of those fantasy sounds which programmers tend to call names like 'cloud nine' or 'glitterball'. Listen to the record and explore what your synth has to offer:

DRUMS

The huge build-up at the end of the intro is articulated by a series of drum fills in free time (i.e. without a strict pulse). Later bars will be hard to align on the sequencer if a regular beat is not maintained, so the fills are printed here to fit into $\frac{4}{4}$ time at 76 bpm.

VERSE & CHORUS

At bar 29 the tempo of the song almost doubles to 136 bpm as the lead guitar launches solo into the eight-bar pattern (A) which forms the basis of the rest of the song. A scaled-down version of this is used to accompany the vocal from bar 45 (B^1 means pattern B with its "first time bar", B^2 uses the "second time bar" instead). There is also a ten-bar pattern to accompany the chorus. The whole song can be assembled by recording the parts for lead, bass, vocal, keyboard and drums, copying the patterns out using the layout diagram below. A slow fade-out on all tracks begins at bar 123.

Bars	29–36	37–44	45–52	53–60	61–70	71–78	79–88	89–96	97–106	107–114	115–122	123–130	131–138
Lead	A	A	B^1	B^2	Chorus	B^2	Chorus	A	Chorus	A	A	A	A
Bass		A	B^1	B^2	Chorus	B^2	Chorus	A	Chorus	A	A	A	A
Vocals			A	B	Chorus	B	Chorus	A	Chorus		C	C	C
Keyboard (starts at bar 42)		A		B	Chorus	B	Chorus	B	Chorus	B	B	B	B
Drums (start at bar 36)	a| Main |b|	Main |b|	Main |b|	Main |b|	Main |c|	Main |b|	Main |c|	Main |b|	Main |c|	Main |b|	Main |b|	Main |b|	Main |b|

LEAD GUITAR

Mark Knopfler's distinctive guitar style has provided him with a parallel career outside Dire Straits as a backing player for many other top artists, including Steely Dan, Van Morrison and Eric Clapton. In *Money for Nothing* he characteristically uses very little distortion, so a clean **rock guitar** voice (GM 28) will probably be your best bet for the lead. His style is rhythmically very incisive and the accents and staccato dots in the score are intended to reflect this. After the massive *crescendo* of bars 21–28, Controller 7 (Channel Volume) or 11 (Expression) should be set at no more than 100 for these patterns, to leave headroom for another *crescendo* at the end of each chorus.

BASS GUITAR   The bass guitar starts at bar 37, following the same patterns as the lead. All eighth notes should be fairly detached, although the quarters are best given their full length.

Pattern A

Pattern B

Chorus

KEYBOARD   Apart from some short stabbed chords to introduce the vocal in bars 42–44, the keyboard part consists of just two patterns to underly verse and chorus. Try **synth brass** on this track.

Pattern A *(bars 42–44)*

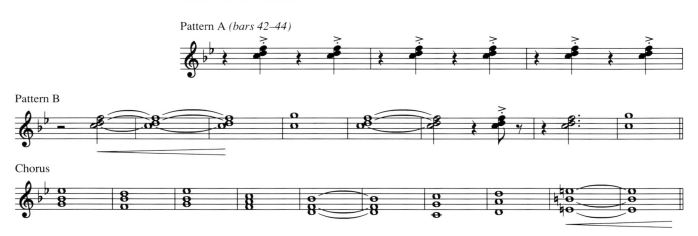

Pattern B

Chorus

DRUMS   Each drum fill forms a link into the next section of music. Fill 'a' (bar 36) introduces the main drum pattern, fill 'b' is the eighth bar of each of the A and B sections, and 'c' fits into the last bar of the chorus. This is a slightly simplified version of the original, which has a wider variety of fills: you may want to elaborate these sections of the track.

VOCALS

There is only space here for an abridged version of *Money for Nothing*, which actually contains several more verses. Knopfler's throw-away singing style is often close to speech in the verses and a purely instrumental version of the song, say on **sax**, will benefit from a reasonably free treatment of the notes printed here. The cross-headed notes in Pattern B reflect pure speech and could be omitted if you are not singing with the sequence. Notice the slow upward slide at the end of the Chorus and remember to set a pitch bend range of two semitones for this.

Pattern A

Pattern B

Chorus

Pattern C

Sequence 15

Be Yourself Tonight

Almost all the songs in this book have been written by men. The distinguished music journalist Simon Frith confesses that "as a man, I've always taken it for granted that rock performances address male desires, reflect male fantasies in their connectons of music and dance and sexuality". The sexist world of Rock & Roll, like most other forms of music, seems to have offered little encouragement to women composers – Carole King is one of the few successful exceptions. However, by 1978 a number of singer-songwriters looked set to follow in her footsteps – notably Kate Bush with her chart-topping debut, Wuthering Heights. *Annie Lennox formed Eurythmics with Dave Stewart in 1980 and they shared the writing of a string of synthesizer-based hits, embacing a variety of styles from electro-pop and soul to a sparse R&B. The song in this chapter is from their 1985 album,* Be Yourself Tonight.

It's Alright (Baby's Coming Back)

Like so much '80s music, *It's Alright* contains an eclectic mix of stylistic influences. The shape of the bass pattern clearly borrows from reggae, and its constant repetition is typical of contemporary dance tracks. However, the chorus vocal comes straight from Soul and the Blues. It contains both the flat 7th (on "*ba* - *by*") and the traditional ambivalence between minor and major 3rd, which Annie Lennox highlights by bending from one to the other on "back" (set a semitone of pitch bend for this). The structure of the song can be laid out as follows:

Bars	1–20	Intro
	21–36	Chorus
	37–52	Bridge
	53–68	Chorus (Instrumental first half)
	69–84	Outro (fade from bar 82)

The original song has an extra Chorus and two more repeats of the Bridge (once as an instrumental and then as a second verse) before the final Chorus and Outro. These could be reconstructed if you wish.

BASS

There are just two bass patterns to underpin the entire song – use a funky **synth bass**. Drums follow a similar format, with a preliminary fill in bar 4:

178 bpm

Words and music by A. Lennox and D. Stewart

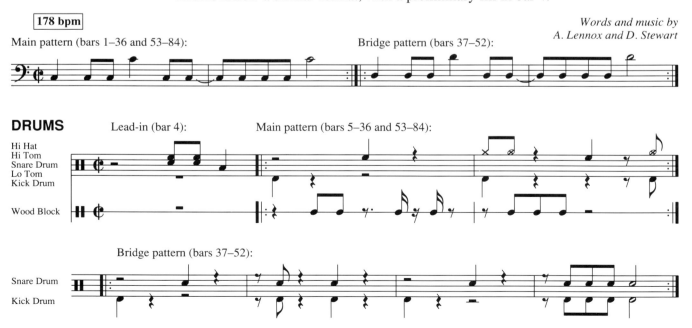

DRUMS

ELECTRIC PIANO

The main pattern needs a sustaining **electric piano** voice and overlaps with the end of the solo in bar 61. Take care not to lose material in this bar when copying. The solo needs to stand out – you may want to use a different sound or transpose the section up an octave to achieve this.

Main pattern (played four times, to fill bars 5–36, and three more times, to fill bars 61–84):

Solo for bars 53–61:

TRUMPET & SAX

All patterns have big crescendos on the long notes. You will need to ensure that the note has maximum velocity (127), then gradually increase Controller 7 (or 11) to open the note up to maximum volume (see Sequence 7 for more information on this). The second pattern is duplicated by a low **sax** an octave below the trumpet. The notes marked ÷ are short and pushed. They will need plenty of aftertouch to "dirty" the sound. Modulation will also add colour to the long notes at bars 18 and 34.

Introduction (bars 9–12):

Bars 14–21 and 30–37:

Bars 46 and 48:

Fade (bars 69–76, repeated to form bars 77–84):

OTHER FILLS

The symbol before the **guitar** chord (below left) indicates notes to be "spread" as an *arpeggio*: play the bottom note first and the others in quick succession, making sure that they are all held down until the end of the bar. The pattern on the right should be voiced for **marimba** and transposed up an octave higher than written:

Bars 37, 41 and 45:

Repeat 8 times to fill bars 37–52:

VOCAL AND BVOX

These parts are of equal importance in *It's Alright* and set up a sort of dialogue in the Bridge. To ensure that they stay clearly audible in the mix, it will help to pan the lead vocal to one side and the bvox to the other.

It's Alright (Baby's Coming Back)

If the mood of your finished sequence seems subtly different from the original, it may be that you are responding to the fact that we have printed the song a semitone lower than the Eurythmics recording, to make it easier to play in. You may wish to transpose the entire song (except drums) back up.

It's Alright (Baby's Coming Back)   *Page 95*

Sequence 16

Experiments with Time

Working through this book, you will have noticed that all the songs so far have at least one basic thing in common – four main beats to the bar. Sometimes these beats are sudivided into threes to give the swing feel of a $\frac{12}{8}$ time signature but, since the '50s, popular music which uses any other format has been as rare as the proverbial intelligent drummer. This is partly a matter of fashion – a century ago the three-time waltz was the most popular dance style and later the foxtrot, which had two beats to the bar, became all the rage. However, it is hard to imagine music with more irregular time signatures ever really entering the mainstream (despite Dave Brubeck's $\frac{5}{4}$ time jazz hit with Take Five) *because the lop-sided feel to the rhythm makes for awkward dancing. Sequencers themselves make no such distinction of course, and remain unfazed by even the most exotic time signature. The following song by Sting is a particularly effective use of $\frac{7}{4}$, transforming the effect of the minimalist techno patterns from which it is built into an entirely fresh sound.*

Straight To My Heart   1985

As with the Eurythmics song in the previous chapter, the influence of sequencing can be heard throughout *Straight To My Heart*. Repeating patterns occur constantly, especially in the bass and marimba parts. However Sting has not simply copied entire verses on their repeat but has cut or shuffled individual bars within the structure to give extra variety. The original song has four verses although you may want to limit your sequence to just the first two if producing a purely instrumental version:

Bars	1–8	9–23	24–32	33–44	Optional additions				45–48	49–52
					45–46	47–55	56–64	65–76	77–80	81–84
Sections	Intro	Verse 1	Verse 2	Bridge	Link	Verse 3	Verse 4	Bridge	Coda	Outro
Copying hints for backing tracks			24–32 are a copy of 13–21	37–40 are a copy of 33–36	Copy of 22–23	Copy of 13–20 plus bar 23	Copy of 13–21	Copy of 33–44		Two copies of 47–48 for fade

The vocal track can be copied in a similar fashion to the backing material, but notice that there are small differences between the verses (especially bars 39–40). The rhythm may also need to be modified to match the words if you are recording verses 3 and 4.

Much of the song can be assembled from basic patterns although we have printed later sections in full because of the increasing number of subtle changes. Note, however, that the two-bar drum pattern remains unaltered throughout – it may be simpler to repeat (or loop) this pattern, rather than risk the danger of splitting the pair of bars when copying and pasting the many sections of the song that have odd numbers of bars.

Through most of the song you will need drums, bass, marimba, vocals and bvox. However, there are also occasional parts for steel drums, electric piano, whistle (or high flute), oboe, strings and extra percussion such as cuica and whip.

Most sequencers now offer as many tracks as you could possibly use – one for each instrument makes editing simple. However, you may find that you run short of MIDI channels on some synths.

TIP Remember that is easy to change a channel's sound in mid track with a programme change message. Many sequencers will also allow you to do this on the "front page" by simply highlighting a particular pattern and assigning a different voice to it. In this song, for instance, a single channel with programme changes could be used for *all* the extra sounds except strings and percussion.

DRUMS

The following two-bar pattern at 164 bpm underpins the entire sequence. 26 repeats of the drum pattern are needed (for the short version of the song). The rim hit on the snare is a light, fairly high-pitched tap rather than an explosive rim shot.

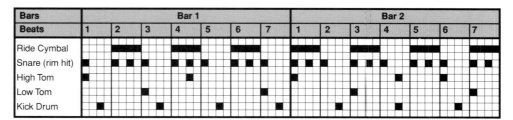

A second drum track should be allocated for the various extra percussion parts that enter during the sequence. The **cuica** is a Brazilian "friction" drum that can produce a hollow sound with a sort of pitchbend effect – a version of this appears on many GM drum lists. Its part, and those for other percussion instruments, are printed in the full score section of the song. However, a quiet **cowbell** appears at the very beginning using the following rhythm (two more bars of this are needed in bars 22-23):

Cowbell

Repeat 4 times, to fill bars 1–4

MAIN PATTERNS

These start in bar 5 and continue until bar 16. You will see from the full score on pages 99–101, that they also appear many more times later in the song.

Marimba

Bass

OTHER PARTS

The **steel drum** makes a brief appearance in bars 3–4 then reappears with a different pattern at bar 41 in the Bridge section. The Intro is completed by quiet sixteenth notes on **electric piano** in bars 5–8..

Steel Drum

Hard electric piano

VOCAL

The upper stave of the music on page 98 is the main vocal part (try **pan flute** on this). It starts at bar 8. The bvox joins the vocal from bar 13 (the lower stave) and would be effective on a soft brass voice. All of the music on both staves, apart from the final eighth-note in bar 16, is also played by **electric piano**. Notice that both verses from here on continue without piano or bvox, as shown in the full score on page 99.

164 bpm

Main Vocal doubling Electric Piano

Words and music by Sting

(1.) In a hun - dred years from now __ they will at - tempt to tell you how __ a sci - en -

Electric Piano

- tif - ic means to bliss __ will su - per - cede the hu - man kiss. __ A

(1.) sub - a - tom - ic chain __ will may - be gal - van - ize the brain, __ or a
(2.) sug - ar - coat - ed pill __ would give our lov - ers time to kill. __ I think they're

Bvox doubling electric piano

Vocal only

bi - o - chem - ic trance __ will el - im - in - ate ro - mance. __ Why -
work - ing far too much __ for the re - dun - dan - cy of touch. __ But

3. If it's a future world we fear,
     We have tomorrow's seeds right here,
     For you can hold them in your hand,
     Or let them fall into the sand.
     But if our love is pure,
     The only thing of which we're sure,
     Then you can play your part
     And fly straight to my heart.

4. If I should seek immunity
     And love you with impunity,
     Then the only thing to do
     Is for me to pledge myself to you
     They only dealt one card,
     So for me it is no hard.
     Your're the bright star in my chart,
     You go straight to my heart.

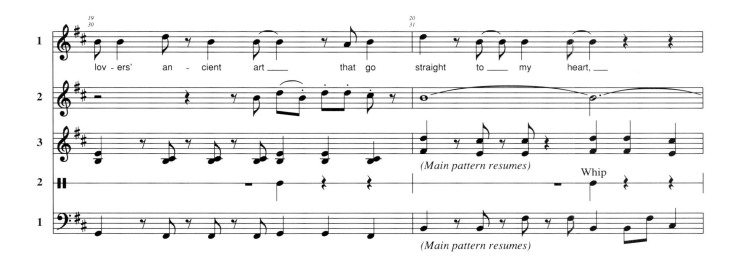

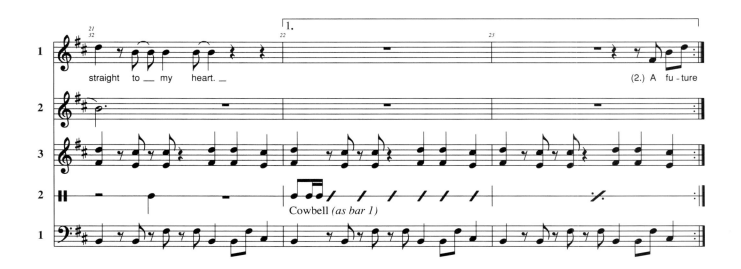

Bridge

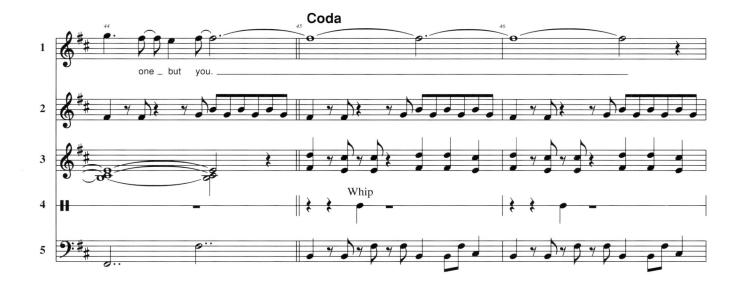

one _ but you. _____

Repeat for fade

Straight   to ___ my   heart, ___   staright   to ___ my   hear.. ___

(Steel Drum)   Oboe

Saturday Night Rave

Club-goers will already be aware that much of the music which energises their Friday and Saturday nights has never been near the mainstream record charts and can usually be heard only on small, specialist radio stations. This is not music to hum along with – its sole purpose is for dancing. Good club DJs are renowned for their ability to splice tracks together seamlessly, often using sampling technology to create their own individual mixes. Contemporary dance music is an area in which independent record labels (which may consist of little more than a couple of people assembling sequences in the spare room) still have huge influence. Rap styles are common, as is the use of sampled fragments of voices or bits of existing records. A bottom-heavy mix and a driving beat are standard, and tempo has increased from around 130bpm for the original Acid House music of the '80s, through the 150bpm of Techno, to 180bpm and above for Jungle. The music is often highly repetitive and those who complain about a certain lack of variety are told, reasonably enough, that they are missing the point. Fashions change quickly so, rather than presenting someone else's music, here are some basic starting points for your own original track.

Dance Basics

Main sections can be constructed from just the simplest material, perhaps two or three chords or a strongly rhythmic bass riff, forming short patterns which are repeated to make 16- or 32-bar units. These are alternated with other sections, often similar in texture and content, which may be based on as little as the repetition of a one-bar riff.

Fade-out endings are universal, but two sorts of Intro are common:
- ➥ a free-time, fantasy-like start which airs some of the material in slow motion before the main beat begins;
- ➥ a "layered" opening at full tempo, in which instruments enter one by one, building up to the entry of bass and kick drum at the start of the first main section.

DRUMS

The driving momentum after this point is created by the interaction of kick drum, rapid hi-hat and bass, occasionally punctuated at the end of sections by elaborate fills. Because this music is almost invariably created using a sequencer, drum parts can be written which would be simply impossible (at 150+ bpm) for a drummer to play live. Here are some possible guidelines:

- ➥ **Kick Drum**: 4 beats to the bar. Generally keeps out of slow Intros and fills. Percussive but bassy sound needed.
- ➥ **Closed Hi-Hat**: try continuous 16th notes, possibly with occasional accents (or open HH) where there are gaps in the bass part.
- ➥ **Hand Claps**: on backbeats (i.e. beats 2 and 4).
- ➥ **Snare**: less prominent than in Rock & Roll, often used for a light fill in every fourth bar, using the off-beats to drive the rhythm towards the next bar. Can also reinforce Hi-Hat 16ths in bigger fills at the end of main sections.

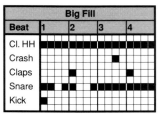

Note that all of the examples in this section are designed merely as a springboard for your own ideas – try customising patterns to the exact sound you want.

BASS AND CHORDS Although the sequence may use two or three chords, the bass often centres around the same note for bars on end, propelling the rhythm forward almost like another drum. Small variations can be made in the bass rhythm, and by introducing new pitches at the end of the patterns (as in bars 1, 2 and 4 below). The xylophone part adds textural interest to what would otherwise be a straight repeat of the first four bars. It is a good idea to design a selection of simple riffs (or find samples) which will fit with your main bass and drum patterns – ways of developing material based on just a single chord can be found on pages 30–33 of *Music in Sequence*.

Contrasting ("B") sections can involve as little as a shift of the bass to a new pitch, perhaps with some rhythmic chords instead of the sustained synth. Be prepared also to write some "stop" bars into your sequence, perhaps as the eighth bar of the B section, in which all instruments are silent. A drum fill in this bar will allow a fresh injection of energy for the return of the main patterns.

Later in the track, when rather more contrast is needed, "breakdown" sections can repeat previous material without bass and kick drum, taking the bottom out of the music for a few bars until a snare fill kicks the track into life again. Synth effects, such as a sweep of Sc-Fi or Crystal, are also often used as section markers.

Vocal parts also tend to be very simple and repetitive: a rhythmically spoken rap or a single-pitch chant often suffice. Chord patterns are not an important part of the style, and some dance music is based almost entirely on a bass lick which can be varied, fragmented and copied by other instruments at different octaves throughout the track:

Full Circle: the 1990s

A common criticism of music in the late '80s was that it had lost its way. The pop charts reflected the continuing popularity of musical survivors from the '70s or even earlier and most new talent seemed unwilling (or unable) to break new ground. Nearly ten years later this tendency towards conservatism has hardened into a definite production value ("retro") and the Number 1 in any particular week may be in any of a bewilderingly eclectic range of styles recycled in various ways from years earlier. The logical outcome of this is a sort of musical cannibalism, and we have now reached the bizarre situation where the most heavily-hyped "new" releases are of out-takes and second rate material by '60s groups like the Beatles and the Rolling Stones which were rejected first time round. Some of the most interesting original work is coming from bands who are putting an ironic "spin" on this obsession with the past.

Blur's album The Great Escape *(1995) follows the theme of urban alienation through the kaleidoscope of styles you might encounter while tuning the dial of a radio. The song in this chapter manages to combine echoes of ballads from the Kinks and the Beatles with a deadpan commentary on life in '90s London. The singing is mournful, the playing deliberately unpolished. If Punk was angry and resentful, this is nearer to desolation. Entirely appropriate, you might think, for the times we live in. However, as we pointed out in Sequence 1, the introspection and stagnation of popular music after the war opened the door for Rock & Roll. Maybe the stage is now being set for a second revolution.*

Recording The Sequence

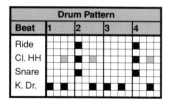

Best Days uses what sounds like an artificially lengthened snare sound to give a surreal hollowness to each backbeat. You may be able to reproduce this by editing the envelope of a standard snare voice. In any case, make sure that the track has an almost insane amount of reverb – a lot of this will be soaked up as later tracks are added.

The pattern shown left forms the basis of the entire song. Bars 1–24 use just the Kick and Snare Drum notes. At bar 25 add the Closed Hi-Hat notes shown in black and, at bar 35, add the Ride Cymbal and the additional Closed Hi-Hat notes printed in grey.

We have printed a slightly shortened version of the song for sequencing. Instrumental parts are reasonably straightforward – a particularly tinny piano sound would be appropriate for the solo at bar 35 (Blur are fond of the sound of trashy electronic keyboards in their mixes). The bleary, trance-like state of the nightworker returning home in the small hours is further reinforced by a banjo part that is deliberately out of tune with the guitar on the recording.

TIP Your synth may allow you to de-tune the banjo individually. If not, programme a very small amount of downward pitchbend onto this track before the music starts and leave it in force throughout the song.

As always, remember that notation must not be taken too literally. For example, while the speed is shown as 72 bpm, Blur gradually increase the tempo on the recording, reaching about 80 bpm by the end. Such subtle alterations can make a big difference to the overall effect, so increment the value by 1 at the start of each new section.

INTRO

Words and music by Damon Albarn,
Graham Coxon, Alex James and David Rowntree

First two bars: drums only

1. Bow bells say good-bye to the __ last train.
2. Cab - bie has his mind on a fare __ to the sun,

2nd verse only:

O - ver the ri - ver they all ___ go a - gain, out in - to leaf - y no - where. _____
he works nights but it's not ___ much fun, picks up the Lon - don yo - yos

Hope some - one's wait - ing out ___ there for them. _____
all on their own _ down So - ho, take me home. _____

(Strings start in this bar)

CHORUS

Oth - er peo -ple wouldn't like to hear you if you said that these are the best ___ days of our lives.

Oth - er peo -ple turn a round and laugh at you if you said that these are the best ___ days of ___ our ___

INSTRUMENTAL

lives,
of ___ our ___ lives.

Piano

Next: three repeats of bars 25–28, to form bars 44–55
Then: repeat bars 29–32, to form bars 56–59 **CODA**

Discography

All sequences in this book have been closely based on the original recordings and we have drawn attention to as many characteristic features and sounds as possible. However, words and printed music alone cannot hope to describe every nuance of a song. If you aim to reproduce the work of the original artists in detail, listening to their records will be essential. If you are more interested in creating cover versions of your own, comparisons will still be valuable and listening to the albums may also introduce you, as it did us, to whole areas of new repertoire. Below we give details of CD versions of each of the songs in this book. The list cannot claim to be complete and, with deletions and re-issues occurring all the time, is unlikely even to remain wholly accurate. Nonetheless, we hope it will steer you in the right direction.

Song Title	Artists	Album / Compilation	Label / Distributor	CD Number
At The Hop	*Danny and the Juniors*	Rockin' with Danny & the Juniors	MCA	3160
		also on At The Hop	Pickwick	PWKS 511
Sh-Boom (Life Could Be A Dream)	*The Crewcuts*	Forever Doo-Wop: Volume 2	Kenwest	KNEWCD 739
	The Chords	Rock And Roll: The Early Days	RCA / BMG	ND 90085
Bony Moronie	*Larry Williams*	Fabulous Larry Williams	Ace Records	CDFAB 012
		also on 100 Hits of the '50s	Tring International	VAR 067
Puppy Love	*Paul Anka*	21 Golden Hits: Paul Anka	RCA / BMG	ND 82326
		also on Million Sellers Volume 7	Disky	MSCD 1907
Please Please Me	*The Beatles*	The Beatles 1962–66	Parlophone / EMI	CDS 797036 2
		also on Please Please Me	Parlophone / EMI	CDP 746435 2
A Whiter Shade of Pale	*Procol Harum*	Portfolio	Chrysalis / EMI	MPCD 1638
		also on Greatest Hits of 1967	Premier / MFP	CDGH 1967
		also on Our Generation	Tellydisc	TELCD 39
He Ain't Heavy … He's My Brother	*The Hollies*	20 Golden Greats: Hollies	EMI	CZ 211
		also on All The Hits and More	Capitol / EMI	CDS 790850 2
		also on Hits of 1969	MFP / EMI	CDMFP 5919
		also on Our Generation	Tellydisc	TELCD 39
Black Magic Woman	*Santana*	Abraxas	CBS / Sony	CD 32032
		also on The Best of Santana	Columbia / Sony	4682672
		also on Greatest Hits: Santana	CBS / Sony	CD 69081
	Fleetwood Mac	Collection: Fleetwood Mac	Castle	CCSCD 157
Stairway to Heaven	*Led Zeppelin*	The Song Remains The Same	Swansong	SK 289402
		also on Classic Rock (Atlantic)	Atlantic / Warner	K 781 935 2
		also on Remasters 1	Atlantic / Warner	7567 80415 2
I Do It For Your Love	*Paul Simon*	Still Crazy After All These Years	WEA / Warner	759 925591 2
		also on Greatest Hits: Paul Simon	CBS / Sony	CD 86047
Money, Money, Money	*Abba*	Greatest Hits: Volume 2	Polydor	8000122
		also on Abba Gold	Polydor	517007-2
Rivers of Babylon	*Boney M*	Greatest Hits of All Time	Ariola / BMG	259.476
		also on The Greatest Hits	Telstar	TCD 2656
	The Melodians	Celebration: 25 years of Trojan	Trojan	CDTRD 413
Hello	*Lionel Ritchie*	Can't Slow Down	Motown Records	MCD 06059 MD
		also on Back To Front	Motown Records	530 018-2
Money for Nothing	*Dire Straits*	Brothers In Arms	Vertigo / Phonogram	824 499-2
		also on Communique	Vertigo / Phonogram	800 052-2
		also on Money For Nothing	Vertigo / Phonogram	836 419-2
It's Alright (Baby's Coming Back)	*Eurythmics*	Be Yourself Tonight	RCA / BMG	ND 74602
		also on Eurythmics Greatest Hits	RCA / BMG	PD 74856
Straight To My Heart	*Sting*	Nothing Like The Sun	A & M	CDA 6402
Best Days	*Blur*	The Great Escape	Food / EMI	7243 8 35235 2 8